WAYS & MEANS

A Collection of Hints & Helps for
Machinists, Metal-workers, Model
Makers, Watch and Tool Makers,
Jewelers, Draughtsmen, etc.

A. H. Cleaves

reprinted by Lindsay Publications Inc

WAYS AND MEANS

FOR

Machinists, Metal-workers, Model Makers, Watch and Tool Makers, Jewelers, Draughtsmen, Etc.

BEING A

COLLECTION OF HINTS AND HELPS NOT FOUND IN BOOKS
USUALLY WRITTEN FOR THIS CLASS OF ARTIZANS.

BY

A. H. CLEAVES, M. E.

With One Hundred and Twenty-five Illustrations.

Ways and Means

by A. H. Cleaves ME

Originally published by
John W. Weston Printing House
Blue Island IL

Original copyright 1892
by A. H. Cleaves ME

Reprinted by
Lindsay Publications Inc
Bradley IL 60915

ISBN 1-917914-75-9

1 2 3 4 5 6 7 8 9 0

1999

WARNING

Write for a complete catalog of unusual books available from:

Lindsay Publications Inc
PO Box 12
Bradley IL 60915-0012

AUTHOR'S PREFACE.

In presenting the following pages, the author frankly states that he has not attempted to lay out his matter with any regard to finished arrangement, but that in gathering up the best records of a broad practical experience and adapting them to present, and so far as possible, future practice, he has rather devoted himself to making the work understood by the readers for whom it is intended, and to present them some facts of mechanical practice and experience never before put in print.

While collating and preparing the matter, the author's attention has been directed to the fact that there are other materials and appurtenances, connected with the mechanics practical work that have not been, by any means, exhaustively treated.

It is therefore, intended that "Ways and Means" shall be the opening book of a series of such handy volumes. which shall possibly include:

"Mechanical Movements Applied," "Gauges, Scales and Measuring Instruments," "Punches, Dies and Die Sinkink," "Mould Making," etc.

It has been the especial aim in the present work to make the matter plain to every mechanic, and the same policy will be pursued in the promised future treatises.

With these few introductory remarks the author begs to leave this little work to speak for itself, but trusts and hopes that enough of interest will be found somewhere in its pages to compensate for the moderate outlay required to secure it.

A. H. CLEAVES.

Chicago, March 1, 1892.

TABLE OF CONTENTS.

CHAPTER V.

THE MODERN BENCH LATHE.

CHAPTER VI.

CHUCKS OF DIFFERENT KINDS.

CHAPTER VII.

SLIDE RESTS AND BENCH LATHE TOOLS.

CHAPTER VIII.

A VARIETY OF WAYS AND MEANS.

CHAPTER IX.

A VARIETY OF MATTER.

CHAPTER X.

UNIVERSAL FORMULA FOR GEARING UP ANY LATHE TO CUT ANY THREAD.

APPENDIX.

x

ALPHABETICAL INDEX.

APPENDIX.

WAYS AND MEANS.

I.

HARDENING AND TEMPERING SMALL WORK.

A knowledge of principles is one thing and that of their application another. The alphabet is quite a simple affair, but its different combinations are wonderful to contemplate.

A treatise on the lever weight and fulcrum might be read with interest by hundreds of persons who would never think of applying the principles of the same, as displayed in the old fashioned method of tightening a saw frame with a wooden slat and a piece of clothes line. And how many who have seen this device hundreds of times, would ever think of using the same to hold in position, while being glued, a broken chair, as shown in Fig. 1?

FIG. 1.

A general idea of spring temper was conveyed by the expiring black-smith to his son, when he said:—Don't forget the cherry-red and the pigeon-blue; but this rule will admit of amplifying.

In order to properly manage small pieces of steel in quantities while being heated, either for hardening or annealing, it will be necessary to have on hand some finely powdered charcoal to pack them in. This can be prepared, if only a small quantity is required, in an ordinary coffee mill, or an improvised mortar and pestle, made of any iron receptacle and crusher nearest at hand.

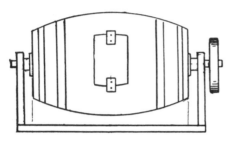

Where it is desirable to prepare and keep on hand a considerable amount of the dust, the appliance shown in Fig. 2 can be used to advantage.

It consists of an ordinary oak barrel, such as is used for kerosene oil or similar substances, having a shaft or axle running through its entire length, and whose projecting ends rest in the bearings of a wooden frame, one of them being sufficiently long to receive a pulley. The barrel is secured to the shaft by means of plates fastened to the ends of the barrel by wood-screws, and to the shaft by set-screws. It has, also, a tight fiting door or cover on its side, securely fastened; the charcoal being confined with a medley of iron castings in the barrel, and the latter revolved.

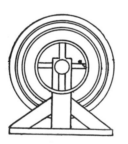

FIG. 2.

The operation is the same as that of tumbling castings.

A smaller barrel or a keg may be employed for the same

purpose, being turned by means of a crank on the grind-stone plan, where the usual motive power is wanting. In addition to the above, a fine sieve, usually made with brass gauze, will be required for sifting the dust very fine. A common flour sieve will answer very well.

For heating work to be hardened, gas-pipe receptacles of various dimensions will be required. These are pre-

The dotted line at top shows
a hollow cap.

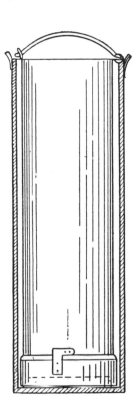

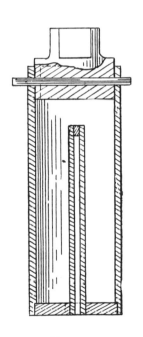

FIG. 3.   FIG. 4.

pared by cutting gas-pipes, varying in diameter from 1½ to 3 inches, into lengths varying from 3 to 8 inches, to be used according to the amount of work required to be hardened at one time.

These pipes are securely sealed at one end, and a taper-ing plug or cap is closely fitted to the other, and secured in place with a tapering pin as shown in Fig. 3. The movable cap is provided with a projecting stem or knob to which the tongs can be applied for removing.

The writer has employed with admirable results, a device for showing when a proper heat is reached, which consists of a small piece of gas pipe secured to the fixed plug in the pipe and extending two-thirds of the length into the center of the same. This small pipe is open at the end fixed in the plug, and sealed or plugged at the inner end. This enables the person heating the work to look into the centre of the receptacle and tell readily when the desired heat is attained, which is generally several minutes after the outside of the pipe is hot.

A word of caution will be very appropriate here: care must be taken that the taper pin holding the cap be driven in securely and taken out carefully. The charcoal contained in the pipe expands, and unless securely confined, will blow out and possibly burn someone.

Do not omit the taper pin, and trust to the friction of the cover for holding the work, as it is not safe. This method of hardening has been employed for years and the only precaution necessary to avoid the above accident or any other, is to be careful in fastening and removing the plug. The taper pin should project sufficiently when driven in to be forced out easily, and should not be removed until the pipe is directly over the hardening tank, when the inverted pipe is held with tongs by one person, while the plug is held in the same manner and the pin driven out by another.

The person holding the cap or plug after driving out the pin and removing the same, raps the bottom of the pipe to remove all the work at once. This should be done at arm's length, as the hot charcoal dust will rise for an instant and the oil will flash; the latter will soon settle down and the blaze can be blown out or smothered by covering the mouth of the tank.

Another thing to be avoided in this proceeding is the use of a hollow cap or shell as shown in Fig. 3; for the hot charcoal dust will be forced through the pin holes, when the pin is removed, in a most vicious manner.

In packing these pipes with the charcoal and work, the latter should be distributed equally through the pipe and be sufficient in quantity with the charcoal to fill the same. If properly packed and emptied into the tank, the steel pieces when hardened, will come out clean and white, and readily show the different shades of color desired in tempering without any polishing or brightening. Screws unless case-hardened should invariably be hardened in oil, if their threads are V-shaped, as they are almost sure to break if hardened in water.

For annealing steel, similar and larger pipes may be employed readily in a small forge; or in a very simple annealing and hardening furnace which will be illustrated further on. Pipes as large as 4 by 17 inches can be used for this purpose and the cap instead of being pinned can be screwed in, and the same if loosened at any time by repeated heating, can be sealed with moistened pipe-clay.

Any steel used in the machine shop, that these pipes will contain, can be annealed thoroughly in this way. A galvanized iron, or similar box, containing a quantity of charcoal dust should accompany the outfit, in which the pipes when thoroughly heated can be covered and allowed to cool gradually. Steel heated in an open forge can be buried in these boxes and quite successfully softened.

The tanks for the oil, Fig. 4, are made as follows: A plain can thirty inches high, and ten inches in diameter for large pieces, and a similar one twenty by eight inches for small work, will be required for the outside or oil tanks. Similar cans with movable bottoms, an inch less in diameter will be needed for removing the steel from the oil. These cans can be made of the heaviest sheet tin, or better perhaps, of galvanized iron. The outside ones can have handles like those on a washboiler, and the inside ones bails, like an ordinary tin pail.

The movable bodies of the inside tanks are about 1½ inches deep, and are in reality strainers, having bottoms of brass gauze.

The steel is cooled effectually by passing clear through the body of oil to the bottom of the inside tank. This when drawn out strains the oil from the work, and after removing the pan, it can be readily cleaned as follows: The steel pieces while in the pan are placed in a larger basin containing benzine, and by shuffling or shaking, the oil is instantly removed. They are then dried by being placed in a fine sieve containing a good supply of fine box-wood saw-dust, which is sifted out into a drawer or receptacle to be used again. A small tight can containing from one quart to a gallon, can be used for holding the benzine, as after being used once it can be returned through a funnel and used repeatedly until too muddy for service. For hardening, good lard oil can be used; the box-wood saw-dust can be had from H. Chapin & Son, Pine Meadow, Conn.

II.

A CHEAP HARDENING AND ANNEALING FURNACE.

Figs. 5 and 6 represent a very convenient and practical furnace, that can be made at a moderate cost, and used without the usual adjunct of a bellows or blower. The only essential in a furnace of this kind is a good draft, such as can be obtained with an ordinary 6-in. stove-pipe properly placed, a connection with the chimney of a boiler being desirable.

The pieces A, B, are iron castings so arranged that the door C, which is the arc of the cylinder, can be opened or closed as a sliding door for the entrance D,—in this way making, when open, a check-draft.

E, E', is the grate used for dumping the ashes and furnishing the draft required. The holes F, F', were introduced in the furnace from which the illustration was taken, to extend the draft to the ends of long pipes, and proved very effective for this purpose, preventing the fault of heating the middle of the pipes only.

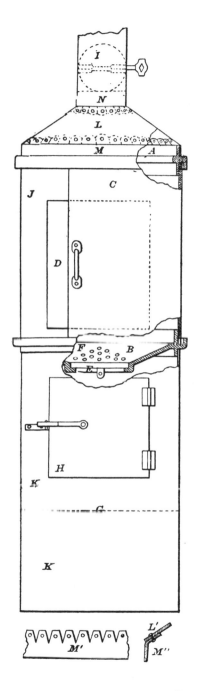

FIG. 5.   Scale ¾ in. = 1 foot.

The dotted line *G,* shows the bottom of the ash-pit, a safe arrangement for hot coals that may sift down. The draft is regulated with the door *H,* and the damper *I,* in the pipe.

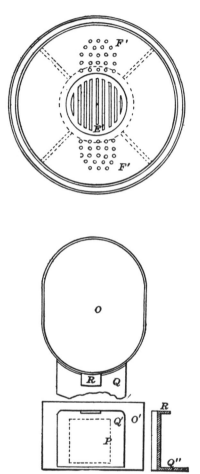

FIG. 6.   Scale ¾ in = 1 foot.

The cylinders *J, K,* are made of sheet-iron about one-twelfth of an inch thick and are fitted to the cast-iron rings *A, B,* as shown. The top *L,* is made of sheet-iron, riveted to the sheet-iron rings *M, N,* as shown at *L, M, N;* and *M', M''.* The ring *L', M, M'* is fitted to the outside of cast-iron ring *A,* as shown.

The sheet-iron fixture O, O', in Fig. 6 will be found very convenient in heating small pipe. It has an opening shown by the dotted lines at P, and is accompanied by a movable door Q, Q', Q'', which can be seized with the tongs at R, and readily moved to allow of examining the work through the opening P, or of turning it while heating.

The top of O, can be wholly or partially covered as needed with another piece of sheet-iron. Any one who has ever tried to keep a small lot of charcoal around a large piece of work, will appreciate this little device, especially if they have been in the habit of buying the charcoal themselves. It banks the coal up closely to the work, concentrating all the heat, and preventing any waste of fuel.

A few words relating to "Bunsen" burners, may not be out of place as a supplement to the description of the annealing and hardening furnace.

A person who has tried to harden or temper very small work in an ordinary forge knows something about the inconvenience and annoyance connected with the attempt; and while such a method is the only one employed in many shops it is always engaged in with a sense of uneasiness and misgiving.

Not unfrequently, after losing track of a small article in the bosom of a charcoal fire, the unhappy person may be seen pawing the coals out, and probing about with a poker, amongst the ashes and filling of the forge; or diving down below the tuyere in search of the missing piece; in some instances finding the same all fire-blistered, and in others not finding it at all.

It is a good plan to use a piece of gas-pipe closed at one end, in heating small pieces in a regular forge. The pipe can be laid in the fire and heated, and the work held in it with a piece of wire or a light pair of tongs. Another method, not at all new, is to heat a dish of lead to the desired temperature, as a kind of bath, into which small delicate articles can be plunged without any danger of overheating. In tempering, a common practice is to

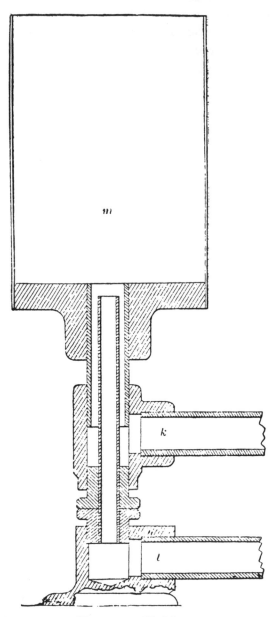

FIG. 7.   Half size.

heat a separate piece of metal, and hold the one to be tempered upon this.

But in places where gas is used for lighting, a number

of simple appliances for heating can be purchased, or made, according to the facilities, that will prove a source of convenience and economy where small drills, screws, springs, etc., are to be hardened.

Fig. 7 is made with gas-fitters material and will heat a piece of half-inch octagon steel one inch of its length in five or six minutes.   The tube for admitting the air is connected with a blower, which answers at the same time for the forge.   A good volume of gas is also required, and

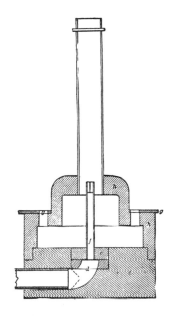

both the gas and air current are regulated by a common faucet or cock.

None of these fixtures are arbitrary, nor designed as a model for a burner to sell; but all the pieces can be purchased ready made of a gas-fitter, or at a supply store, without the trouble of getting up any patterns.

Fig. 8 represents another improvised affair, which, though not intended as a commendable pattern, has proved very effective and convenient. The body was made of a surplus two cone pulley casting, and the pipe

FIG. 8.

of brass tubing.   Quite a little experimenting was required, in making this, to get the proper proportion of air for the gas, as well as finding the proper height of gas-pipe and size of hole in the same for entrance of gas.

In trying a burner of this description, whatever the amount of heat expected, it is best to commence with a very small hole for the gas, perhaps the size of a cambric needle, and open it as required.

Then by admitting the air as required, in position and quantity, the desired result can generally be obtained.

A good head of gas will be required for good work.

The gas for this burner, which will heat a soldering-copper 3½-in. by 1-in., in from five to ten minutes, is taken from an ordinary gas-pipe for lighting, with the lava-tip removed; a power blower not being used.

By inserting a hand blow-pipe at one of the openings (a, Fig. 9), an intense heat can be projected on small objects held in the cupola (Fig. 9). By taking off the latter,

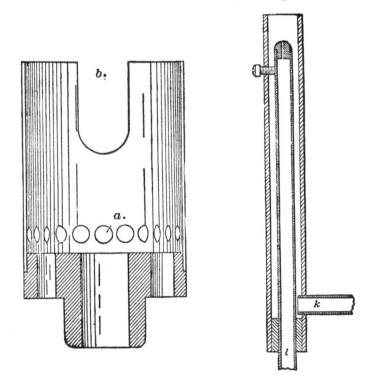

FIG. 9.   (Half size)   FIG. 10.

and placing small pieces to be heated, on a piece of charcoal held in the hand, and using the blow-pipe, the same can be done very conveniently.

By placing the work on one piece of charcoal or asbestos, or in a cavity of the same, and covering it with another piece of the same material, a pretty good sized chunk can be readily heated.

Fig. 10 is a burner to be held in the hand, and moved at convenience; and like Fig. 7 is used in connection with the power blower. The one used in this instance is a Sturtevant, "Cupola and Forge" blower No. 1; but that is immaterial. This last burner makes a small fine jet, which is very serviceable for hardening small saws, and thin pieces of work held on charcoal.

Any one desirous of purchasing burners of improved design and price, can probably find what they require at E. H. Sargent & Co.'s 125 State street, Chicago, or with F. W. Gesswein, No. 39 John street, New York.

The samples furnished in the illustrations however, though prepared on a kind of a go-as-you–please plan, have been pretty well tested, and proved cheap and effective; and will probably furnish a clue, at least, to any one who wishes to secure a home-made article.

A burner like Fig. 8 with cupola Fig. 9, will furnish a mould-maker or watch-repairer with quite a complete hardening and tempering apparatus; and it can be made at a small cost by almost any machinist. The opening at b, in the cupola is intended to place the soldering-copper in while being heated; and can also be used for work to be heated, as described, with a blow-pipe.

The base c, is made of wood, and arranged at d, to allow the free entrance of the gas; e, being a metal base for the pipe f. The piece g, is a sliding ring or damper for regulating the air supply, and has holes and spaces to cover similar openings in the casting h.

A few hints and appliances relating to hardening and tempering small pieces with these burners may be new and acceptable to some of our readers. Where circular saws, not over $3/64$ of an inch thick, are to be hardened, it is customary, whether heating them in a lamp or the forge to cool them by placing, when hot, between two perfectly flat pieces of iron, smeared with lard-oil. The saw is heated on a piece of charcoal, or if in the forge on a thin piece of strip steel or iron, and dropped quickly onto one iron block, when the other is instantly seized and pressed

on to it.   This both hardens the saw and preserves its flat
shape.   They are then brightened and tempered as required.   In another place the writer intends to give a description of fixtures used for grinding small circular saws,
and methods of doing the work.

For tempering various kinds of brightened work over a
lamp or burner it will be found very convenient to have
a small box-shaped copper pan V, with handle like that in
Fig. 11.

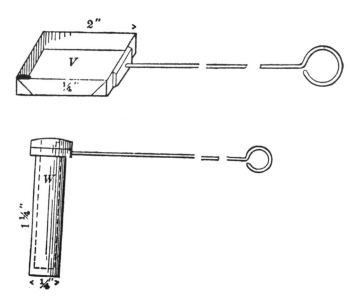

FIG. 11.

For hardening very small drills or pieces of steel, with
a lamp or burner, it will be found a good plan to make a
small copper tube with a handle like W.   This can be
held in the cupola of Fig. 8 (see 9,) and heated with the
blow-pipe, and at the same time watched by the operator.

In this way a piece of steel or several pieces no longer
than a cambric needle can be heated without the least
danger of being burned.

For drawing the temper on very small springs a small
box made of copper can be used; burning the oil from the
outside of the box as in spring tempering.

For Fig. 7 a ⅝-in. rubber pipe or hose, any desired length, is used; and the gas enters at k, the air at l; which applies as well to Fig. 10. In the latter the pipes, k, and l, should be left about two inches long for rubber pipe.

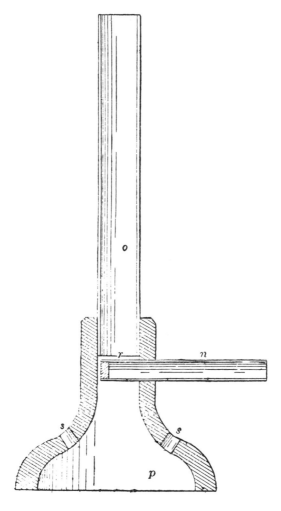

FIG. 12.   Half size.

On Fig. 7, m, is a cupola which for convenience should be made like Fig. 9, movable.

Fig. 12 is a very cheap yet efficient burner, which can probably be purchased as cheaply as made, unless the person wishing to use it has tools and material convenient for making one; *n*, and *o*, are regular size brass tubing, and *p*, is a cast-iron base.   The gas enters through a small hole at *r*; and *s, s*, are holes made in sufficient number to supply the air.

A burner of this description, about the size of the drawing, can be used frequently, to advantage, in the place of a small spirit lamp by dentists, watch repairers, etc.

For hardening small drills and keeping them straight at the same time, a small copper tube, sealed or closed at both ends, can be used; the whole thing being plunged into water.   Hair springs for watches, closely wound into small copper boxes, or capsules, are hardened in this way. This is only warranted on a small scale however.

It will be found very convenient to have a table or stand, made of sheet iron about $1/16$ of an inch thick, and four or five inches in diameter, to use with Fig. 8 or 12; for tempering, tinning plates, heating glue-pot, etc., etc.

With Fig. 9 this should stand about three or four inches above the top of the burner, or better still, be made adjustable.

III.

HARDENING AND ANNEALING.

Before leaving the subject of hardening, etc., mention should be made of a plan for securing an even temper on saws where they are one inch or more in diameter.

To obtain this result it is a good plan to use between the two blocks for hardening, two pieces of metal, saw blanks, for instance, of the same thickness as the one to be hardened.   This will insure a contact of the block with the whole surface of the saw or flat piece to be hardened, as the two blocks will be parallel.   Place two pieces the thickness of the saw at the two similar corners of the block and the saw at the opposite end, the centers of the pieces will then form a triangle and the two blocks will come together as described, parallel.   See *A*, *A'*, Fig. 13.

A pair of tongs, the same as shown in Fig. 14, has been used quite successfully for hardening saws about three inches in diameter.   The saws are heated first and then placed in the tongs, the channels or grooves allowing the water to circulate freely over the surface of the saw.   *a*, is a central hub for locating the saw.

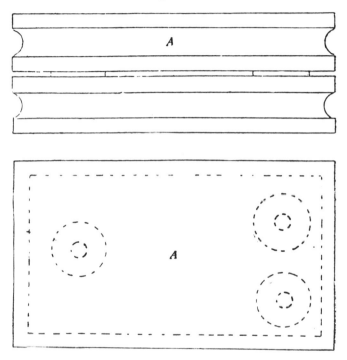

FIG. 13.

Plane irons can be hardened between the blocks, as shown above, and kept very flat at the same time.   The writer has hardened one in water and curled it nearly a tenth of an inch, rehardened it between oiled blocks of cast iron and restored it to a perfectly flat shape.

Figure 15 illustrates a convenient double tank for hardening small pieces, and can be made of brass tubing or, more cheaply, by using two tin boxes like yeast cans.   The line *a*, represents a brass sieve, and the whole thing is a

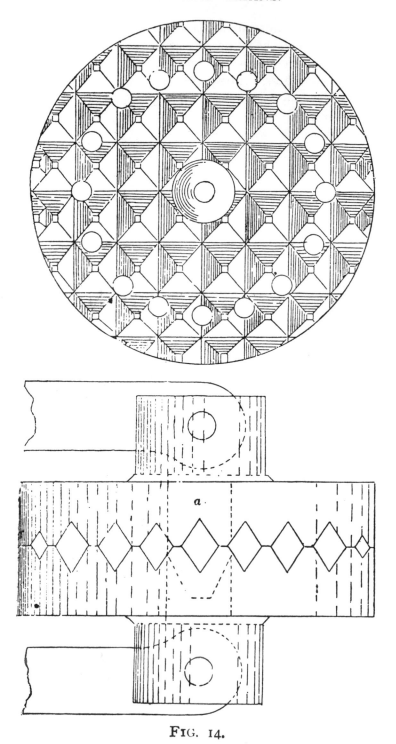

FIG. 14.

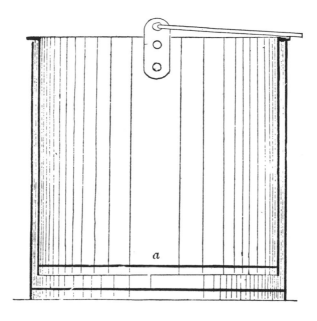

FIG. 15.

miniature device like the tanks shown in Fig. 4.

Fig. 16 is a further illustration of a burner similar to the

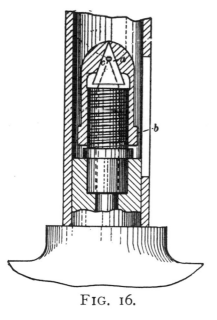

FIG. 16.

ones shown in Figs. 7 to 12. This one furnishes a convenient adjustment for the flame, and, while expensive, may be more acceptable to any one desiring something more elaborate than the others. a, is an adjustable cap, and is knurled at b, so that it can be turned on the threaded burner through the orifices in the outer tube. There are three of these. The burner is opened at c, by drilling small holes in the

tip, which enter the larger opening below,
and the flow of gas is regulated by the
cap *a*, from the holes, *c*.   The taper
cone must be well fitted to the taper-

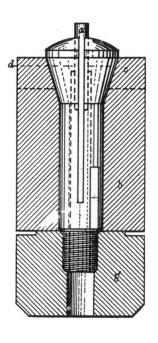

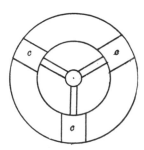

FIG. 18.

ing hole in the cap.   The whole is made
of brass.

Fig. 17 illustrates a very delicate burner for jewelers' and repairers' use.

FIG. 17.

This is made of brass throughout and explains itself. The gas enters the finest of openings at a; and the air comes in at the holes b; c, being a shell or guard to prevent a too violent entrance of air at b, from a gust of wind.

Fig. 18 shows a device that has been used extensively for holding spring chucks while being hardened, although there is not much risk in dipping small chucks into the water without any support, as they require to be hardened but a short distance from the face. a, is a steel plug or piece of wire the size of opening in chuck: and, b, b', are cast-iron pieces which draw the jaws of the chuck together upon the pin a, and prevent its springing when being cooled. c, c', represent openings in the holder to allow the water to approach the chuck near the slots in the same. The dotted line, d, shows about the proper distance from the face that the chuck should be hardened.

In connection with hardening it will be well to say that the best preventive of springing and warping is proper forging and annealing. The hammer must be evenly applied, and before taking the finishing cut on steel work that is to be hardened, it is a good plan to bring it close to the required size and then anneal it carefully.

In hardening irregular shaped work it is best to dip the thickest part first: as the heavy part sets and keeps the rest in form. A knife-blade, for instance, should be dipped back first; and a punch of any kind butt-end first, when practicable.

Steel spindles, etc., that have sprung slightly, can frequently be straightened sufficiently for grinding true by placing in the vise and heating moderately with a lamp or burner while in position, and then applying pressure enough to correct the spring. They are held in the vise between three wires, bent to rest on the jaws of the vise, two at the ends of one vise-jaw, and one at the middle of the other, on the opposite sides of the spindle.

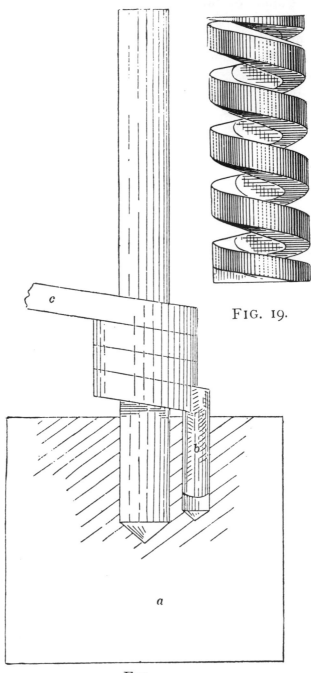

FIG. 19.

FIG. 20.

Heat the spindle to the flat iron requirement, or until it hisses when salivated.

Where a spring temper is not objectionable the work can be heated to a sky-blue and bent quite perceptibly.

A very good plan in hardening is to have an assistant pour cold water through a tube or pipe with its end in the hardening tank, so as to produce a bubbling agitation at the surface of the water in the latter, or else blow through a pipe into the water.

And bevel or irregular shaped cutters, etc., when being hardened should be dropped, when hot, upon a disc at the end of a rod or wire and plunged in this position into the water.

Another thing to be avoided is sharp corners in work to be hardened. Round them if possible if but a little. The bottoms of teeth in cutters when made this way are less liable to crack. Holes in steel pieces, especially if near their edges, should be plugged tightly with wire, or pipe clay, to prevent cracking in hardening.

Pipe-clay or a wet cloth wound around a piece of steel, is of advantage in hardening, or annealing on the end, etc., where it is not desirable to heat the whole piece. Use a blow–pipe in heating. Sometimes it is desirable to make a steel spring about the size and proportion shown in Fig. 19. This kind of spring, made of square steel is used frequently in sub-presses for pushing the punchings out of the die.

Where but a limited number is required they can be made quite conveniently as shown in Fig. 20, which is drawn to the true size that such springs have been made. A cast-iron block, *a*, can be held in the vise and the arbor and spring can be removed from the block together after the first heating. The end, *b*, of the spring is rounded and bent first, and when hot several winds are given on the arbor. The end *c*, can be held in a hand-vise, and by making the springs on steel two or three feet in length they can be handled comfortably without the tongs for a while. In heating care should be taken to have the part nearest the coil hottest. After winding, the springs can be opened to any desired width with a cold-chisel, and turned and finished nicely on the ends by soldering on to another arbor. Being short and stiff this can be reamed out to fit a spindle or arbor, and require to be wound right-handed, so that in facing off the ends in lathe the tool will not cut against the direction of coil.

In ye olden times springs were wound in this manner; and a very ingenious device obtained in the shape of a vise-nut and screw by the same process. Two pieces of steel were wound together and then unscrewed, a part of one piece being cut off and brazed into the vise for the nut; and the other, being brazed onto an arbor, served as the screw. The old timers could probably give us some excellent hints on the construction of such appliances.

- - -

IV.

MECHANICAL APPLIANCES AND METHODS OF VARIOUS KINDS.

Figures 21-22 illustrate a very useful fixture for grinding purposes. *a* is a chuck of the dimensions used in an American Watch Tool Co.'s machinist's bench lathe. In this instance the piece, *a*, is solid, and made of soft steel. *b*, is made of brass, and like *d*, which is made of steel, and spring tempered, can be made in a number of sizes. The piece, *b*, has three set-screws, like *e*, equally distant on the circumference; and can be moved a limited distance on *a*, and adapted to the thickness of saws or cutters like *f*. *d*, is hardened and slotted in three places as far back as, *g*; drawn to a spring temper at *g*, and left hard at *d*, where it comes in contact with the work. Saws and cutters usually run in regular sizes at the center opening, say .20″ .25″ .35″ and .50″;* where decimal sizes are used, and the pieces, *d*, can be made

---

*(″) This sign is used for inches.

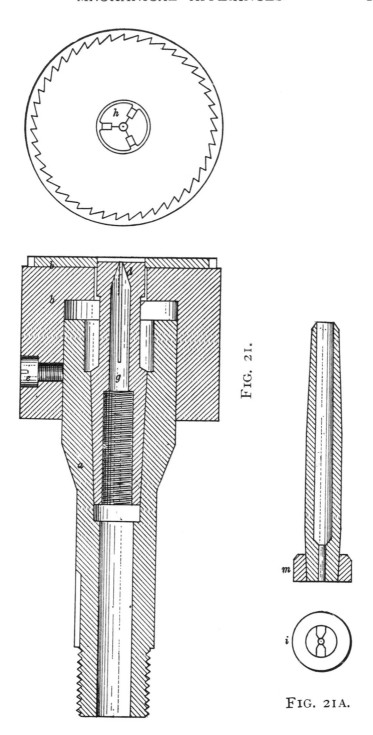

FIG. 21.

FIG. 21A.

these sizes at, *d*. The end view, *h*, of *d*, shows a convenient and practical way of slotting this and other chucks, a large saw or cutter being used to prepare the way for a small one. This leaves but little stock for the thin saw to cut, and at the same time retains the form of small hole in the center of chuck.

Right here it will be a good time and place to mention a way of slotting very small

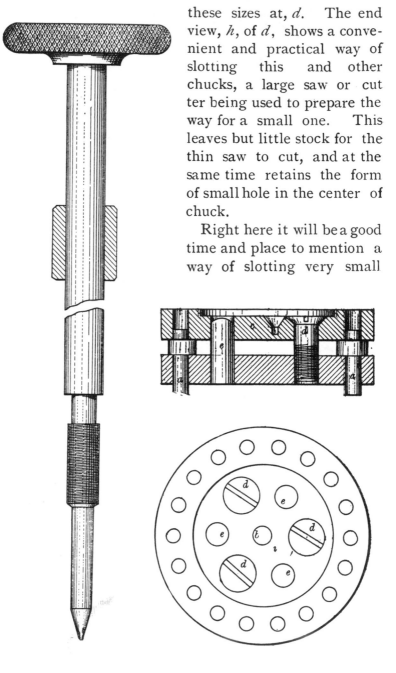

FIG. 22.   FIG. 23.

and delicate chucks, such as are used for holding fine drills, etc. Suppose a drill no larger than the smallest cambric needle is to be used in a split chuck, it can be readily seen that a very small saw with square shaped teeth, though entering from opposite sides of the chuck, would cut the hole for needle drill quite out of shape; while such a saw would hardly admit of being used at all. A cutter, however, V shaped on the edge, made very sharp, would meet the requirements here like a charm, as shown on an enlarged scale at, i, Figure 21A. m, is a taper collar for closing chuck onto drill.

Where such a drill is to be used but a limited time it can be soldered into a small brass taper chuck as well as any way;—an adjustable chuck being desirable where a good many drills are required to do constant service.

Figure 22 shows the spindle or rod with taper point for expanding the jaws of chuck at, d, Fig. 21. The length is determined by the length of draw-in-spindle to lathe. k, is a collar fitting closely in back-end of draw-in-spindle to guide the rod and steady it. This appliance is used in connection with a right-angle emery-wheel grinder, for grinding saws and cutters on the sides.

It can be seen that for all practical purposes it is very reliable and convenient. The face of b, can be trued off readily, and this furnishes a support for the saw and a good resistance to the emery-wheel; while the jaws, d, have but little tendency to strain the work while holding it.

For the most accurate results, however, the only reliable plan is to solder the work upon a solid chuck, trued on the face without removing from the lathe before finishing work.

In grinding thin saws of an inch or more diameter one thing is important, viz: to grind the scale off of concave side first, (the saw being dished in hardening), following the surface and not trying to straighten the same. Then grind the convex-side in the same way, and the work corrects itself; so that another grinding on each side will

hold its shape. Grinding the convex side first will produce a continual springing of the saw.

Small thin saws held between a concave and a convex
washer will be dishing, and will slot small screws, etc., on
an angle, much to the puzzlement of the persons watch-
ing the machine sometimes. Have the faces of the
washer perfectly flat.

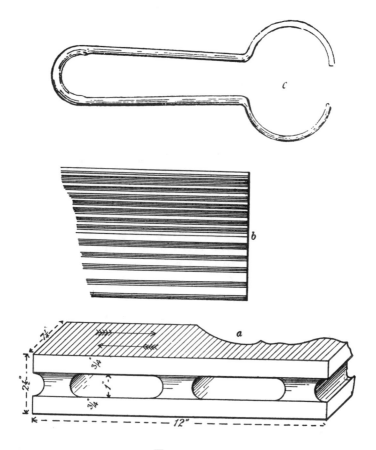

FIG. 23A.

Figures 23 to 26 relate to flat-steel work; and while
they come far from covering all the ground, will give a
general idea of how this kind of work is done. Fig. 23
shows one way of holding a number of pieces similar to
a, a, while being ground and polished on the extreme

ends. A number of such pieces, say seventeen, as shown in *b*, are clamped in position with block, *c*, held in place by screws, *d*, and dowell-pins, *e*.

These blocks are generally made in sets of from six to twenty, according to the quantity of work required. It is important that they be of uniform thickness throughout the set, as the work is measured under an upright gauge; and, for convenience, should gauge to one standard.

Fig 24 shows another kind of work, and this is secured

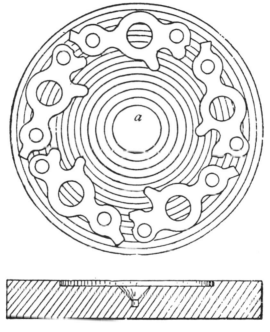

FIG. 24.

to the blocks with shellac. The lines in *a*, are fine grooves into which the shellac fastens itself while hot, and under pressure. Larger grooves, or holes are made to receive any projections on the pieces to be ground. Fig. 25 illustrates a small hand-press used for squeezing the work into position on the blocks in the hot shellac. The drawing is one-fourth size, and shows all the parts except a guide pin and groove in the plunger or spindle which prevents its turning around.

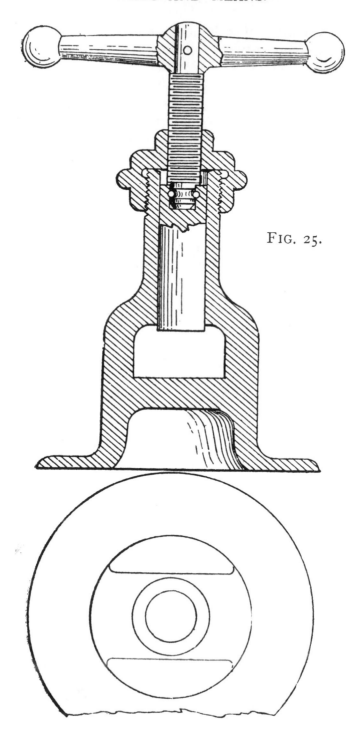

Fig. 25.

The work is laid on the blocks, which are then put on a table over a double-tube heater like those shown in another place; and when sufficiently hot to melt shellac, the same is rubbed or melted onto them, and they are then placed in the hand-press until cool enough to hold in position. When ready to press, several thicknesses of paper saturated with lard or some other oil are laid on the blocks, and between these and the press-plungers a leather pad secured to another steel block is placed, which adapts itself to any irregularity in the work and presses it flat on the blocks.

A great variety of work is finished in this way and the requirements of different kinds will suggest themselves to the mechanic.

Fig. 26 gives an idea of some of the implements used in doing this kind of work by hand; the bulk of it being done by rotary machines run by power. These are too complicated to introduce into a work of this kind, and are made in a number of different styles. A plain wooden handle similar to m, with short steel point for entering the centers, i, can be used alone; or the same attached to the pole, n, can be employed. In this way a foot-pressure is secured on the work by means of the treadle, o, and a rod, p, attached to wooden arm, r. The pole, n, takes the pressure from this, and the only exertion required at m, m', is of a horizontal kind; sufficiently exhilarating and muscle developing, however, to suit the most exacting. The rack $k k'$, and catch s, s', s'', in conjunction with the stiff spring, w, enable the operator to fasten the pole under pressure and remove his foot from the treadle while pushing the work.

The block, t, is of different material for different operations. Cast-iron blocks, about $8'' \times 12''$ with parallel grooves planed in them are used with emery and oil for the first grinding. Then the work is "greyed" or ground smooth on a glass lap, under the pole, with oil-stone dust and oil.

The polishing is then done on boxwood blocks, gener-

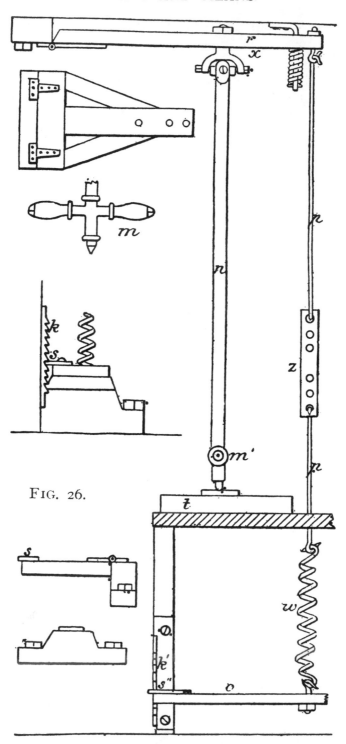

FIG. 26.

ally against the grain, or on the ends of the blocks, with Vienna lime and alcohol.

The boxwood blocks when glued must be made with care and a very little glue, or else they cause trouble. Boxwood coming in logs of small diameter it requires to be split and put up in sections. The writer has tried, with the best results, the plan of facing off the sides of the sections on an angle-iron on lathe face-plate; holding them together with welded iron straps. These are driven down as the blocks are turned off on the ends; being turned off as they wear out of shape. No glue is used in this way and as the blocks always have to be water-soaked, they swell and fit the straps, while the sections come closely together.

Fig. 23A illustrates at *a*, the cast-iron block spoken of, and *b*, shows the style of shallow grooves planed in such blocks. These grooves at *b*, are actual size, being varied to meet the requirements of different sized work. The latter are propelled forward and back on the block across the grooves as shown by the arrows. *c*, shows a simple pair of tongs made of steel wire for handling the blocks in heating.

A large cast-iron block similar to, *a*, is used for lapping flat the glass blocks, emery wheels, etc. The grooves are deeper and further apart however, and coarse sand or emery is used for cutting.

For the large blocks a casting with open space, or box form underneath, strengthened with webs is used 30″ × 17″ × 4½″; and the grooves are $\frac{5}{32}''$ wide × ½″ deep with ½″ space between; cored out 3″ underneath, with 2 webs endways, and 4 crossways. The same kind of block is used for surfacing Water of Ayr stones.

On Fig. 26 the toggle-joint, *x*, admits of traversing the whole surface of the block with the work, and wearing the same evenly; while the strip, *z*, is for adjusting the length and pressure of, *p*, *p*, rod.

Figures 27 to 34 give ideas of various kinds of binders or fastening devices that have been tested and found thor-

oughly practical, though some of them are not especially
novel.

It is intended in presenting these fragments of mechan-
ism to furnish some primary principles and mechanical
movements, that will ad-
mit of a wide diversity of
application, and perhaps
prove acceptable in more
instances than one, to
model and tool-makers
more especially.

In seeking any particu-
lar result of a mechanical
nature, the consideration
of a few practical questions

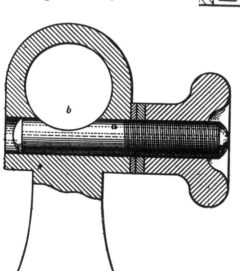

FIG. 27.

will frequently save
a great amount of
study. It is well
to inquire if speed is
required, and to re-
member that it is
obtained generally
FIG. 28.   with a sacrifice of
power. So it is
well to ask about the distance required and the space to
be occupied; and whether an operation is to be perform-
ed¸but a few times or continuously.

These points will be better appreciated when spoken of in connection with the figures.

Fig. 27 shows a familiar method of binding a lathe tail-stock spindle, and explains itself.   The slot a, is sawed but a part of the way through the tailstock lengthwise.

Fig. 28 is a binder for the same purpose, and is used in Mr. Mosely's watch-makers' lathe. a, is a plain piece of

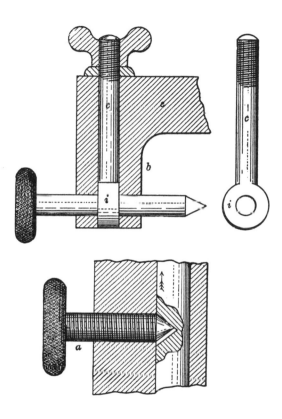

FIG. 29.

wire or steel rod threaded on one end, and milled out at b, to fit the spindle, which cut, serves to bind the same, as well as to keep a, from revolving.   In both of these in-stances the distance traversed is quite limited, and the power exerted in a small space is considerable, and can be increased by inserting a pin or handle into the nuts.   A

screw or nut for these effects is good where they are only
used at intervals; but where repeated operations are required it is better to employ a cam or wedge as will be
shown.

Fig. 29 shows two ways of holding work rigidly.   In *a*,
the point of screw entering the cavity above the center
forces the spindle in the direction of the arrow.   In *b*, the
eyelet or loop of *c*, holds the spindle or center very firmly.
The frame *e*, is drilled for *c*, and milled crosswise for the

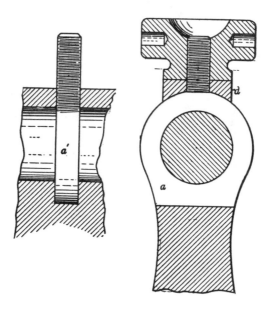

FIG. 30.

loop *i*. *b*, is a very effective binder for small spindles, like
wig-wag centers.

In Fig. 30, *a*, illustrates the same principle applied to a
larger piece, the washer *d*, adapting it to the curved surface of the tail-stock.

Fig. 31 is a powerful eccentric pin, used quite extensively by Mr. Webster and others for securing lathe heads
and tail-stocks to their beds.   There is no weak spot in
this device when properly made; and in order to do this it
is only necessary to have the point *a*, in contact with the

top of slot when the eccentric pin is at its most effective place.

Fig. 32 shows a binding and adjusting device for a tool-holder both in one. The end view *a*, gives the eccentric holder with slots made so as to admit of binding the tool in any position. This is shown solid in *b*, but the slots should be cut something over half the length of *c*. The

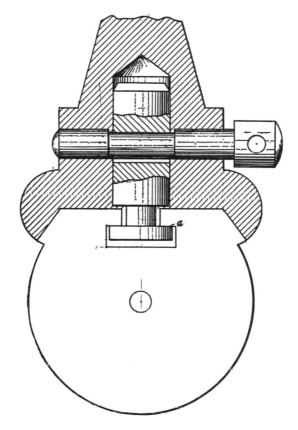

FIG. 31.

cutter being round, can be adjusted a short distance up and down by turning the holder *c*.

Fig. 33 is a good illustration of the economy of space. Advantage is taken of the room lengthwise of the arbor to use the screw, which is seldom removed. *a*, *a'*, are sections of short pieces of wire adapted to the tapering end

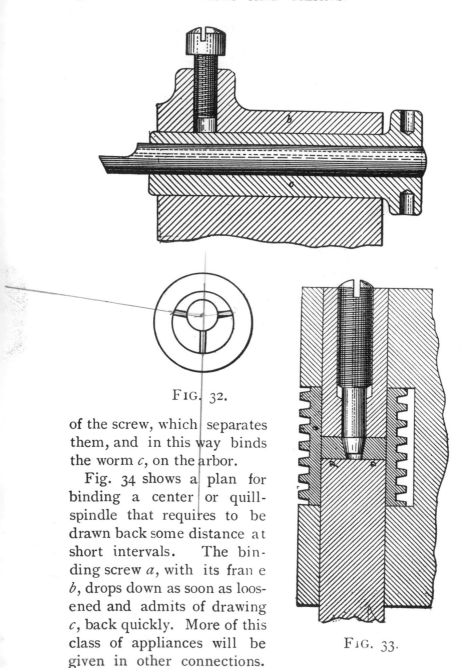

FIG. 32.

of the screw, which separates
them, and in this way binds
the worm *c*, on the arbor.

Fig. 34 shows a plan for
binding a center or quill-
spindle that requires to be
drawn back some distance at
short intervals. The bin-
ding screw *a*, with its frame
b, drops down as soon as loosened and admits of drawing
c, back quickly. More of this
class of appliances will be
given in other connections.

FIG. 33.

Fig. 35 is a useful little fixture that will recommend itself to any one who has tried to cut small taps or screws in

an engine-lathe, and has been compelled to use a clumsy follow-rest. *a*, is an eccentric collar fitted to the tail-stock spindle of an engine-lathe.

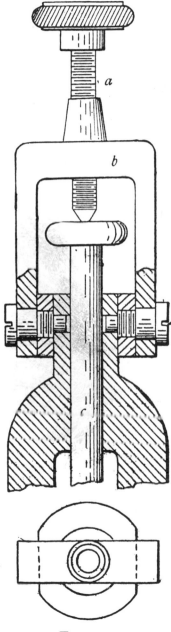

It is provided with a sliding arm *b, b'*, fitted to a groove on the top. This has a slot *c*, for adapting the rest endways, and the pin or bar *d*, made of wire or steel rod, flattened on one side is adaptable to different diameters. *d*, has a V shaped notch in its end. The collar *a*, is furnished with two setscrews as shown. Further comment is needless. Small dogs or drivers, and special face-plates or holders can be adapted to the center in head-stock for carrying delicate work.

Fig. 36 is a mould for forming emery sticks, or plugs, such as are used in grinding the sides or faces of balance arms. The drawing is ½ size. *a*, is made of cast iron. *b*, is a steel shell or tube of the required dimensions, highly polished and very hard. *c, c*, are steel plungers of different lengths for compressing the emery and pushing the plugs from the mould.

They fit the tube closely. Oiled paper comes between the steel plugs and the em-

FIG. 34.

ery, the latter being mixed with silicate or liquid glass.

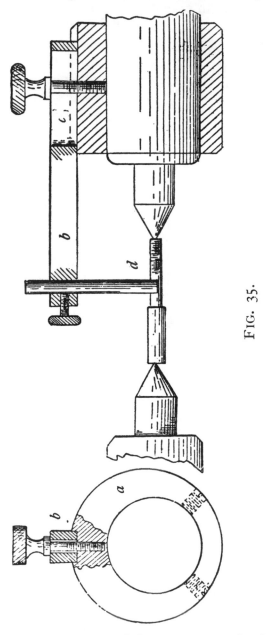

FIG. 35.

The proper consistency of the paste must be found by a
little experimenting. They can be pressed in a hand

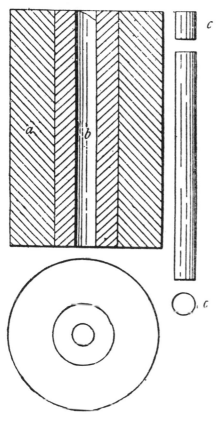

FIG. 36.

screw-press, and dried over the boiler, they are then ready for use.

Fig. 37 shows a countersink and burnisher combined. A small flat disc with sharp corners is seen at *a*, *a'*, which will cup or countersink a hole; while *b*, *b'*, another disc of the same diameter as *a*, having a rounded edge will burnish the cut. *b*, should be highly polished, and both discs left very hard. The handle *c*, is made of pinion-wire of any convenient length, which can be obtained in foot lengths at the supply stores. These tools are sold by the dealers in sets of three or four

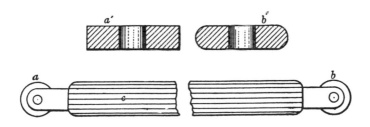

FIG. 37.

different sizes, nicely cased. They are used mostly for brass.

Pinion-wire of different sizes is very convenient for making screw-drivers. (See Fig. 37 A.) The blades can be put in straight and soldered, or on a taper like *a*. The top *b*, is made of hard rubber or box-wood, and held with

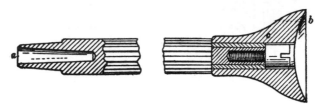

FIG. 37A.

a washer riveted on to the wire, or with screw against shoulder in the cap. In the one illustrated the little sleeve *c*, turns freely under the screw, and the cap fits on to it friction tight.

Fig. 38 is a useful little device for holding drills etc. The screw *a*, can be made on the end of a handle like *b*, of proportionate length and then the holder makes a good

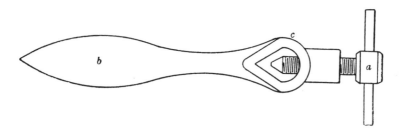

FIG. 38.

tap-wrench for small work. Or the part *c*, can be made of two sizes one at each end of a handle about 4 inches long.

A tool like this made nearly twice this size is very convenient for holding twist drills in a regular machine shop. Drills as large as $5/16$ can be easily handled.

Fig. 39 shows a convenient little tool that meets the requirements where quite a number of small counterbores or screws are to be made, and some inexpensive method is desired.

One of the disadvantages constantly felt in a small factory, and comparatively missed in a large one, is the necessity of producing work, economically, in quantities large enough to require special methods, yet not enough to call for special machines: expensive machines which require constant use to make their purchase or manufacture profitable.

In large factories labor can be distributed to better advantage than in small ones, as the different pieces are made in sufficient numbers to keep one person and one

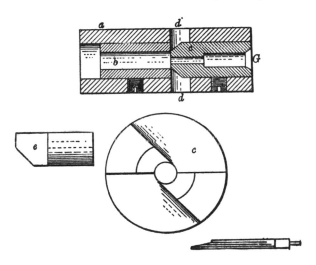

FIG. 39.

machine continually occupied on a few parts, and a few operations; and sometimes on one operation.

Another advantage secured, to the manufacturer at least, by this result is the proficiency acquired by the operator in his particular line of work. The writer was acquainted with an employe in a watch-factory who earned seven or eight dollars a day poising balances. This was double what several others made at the piece-work prices, and more than any foreman in the factory received.

In Fig. 39, a, is a hollow cylinder or receiver for b, and c, b, is a guide for the wire, and c', a hollow mill which cuts the point or teat on the counterbore. c', gives an end view of the latter enlarged. d, d', are outlets for the chips to escape through.

The guide pieces and cutters can be made in different sizes for the same holder.

Jewel-screw counterbores made in this way on wire the right-size for outside of counterbore come very true. They are cut off in lots, and pointed with cutter like e, held in a. The wire is held in a running chuck and the tool pushed against it with the lathe center at G.

The teats of counterbores made in this way are sure to be true with the body and of uniform size; which is not the case when turned in a chuck unless the latter is perfectly true. The end of counterbore is flattened to hold it in its socket, and the sides are milled off to the size of teat by pushing the piece along a grooved guide against two saws running on one arbor, and separated by a washer the thickness of counterbore teat.

The advantage of a tool like this will be better appreciated when it is understood that the actual size of the counterbore teats is only about one hundredth and a half, and quite long in proportion.

This makes pretty small work for a slide-rest, and when made in a staff-lathe, as formerly, they come very defective in size and shape. The cutting lips of the counterbores, of course, are backed off very nicely by hand.

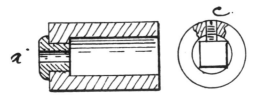

FIG. 40.

Fig. 40 is a simple jig for drilling square or oblong pieces of uniform size in the center. Where a large number of pieces of the same size are to be centered this makes a cheap and accurate tool. If many pieces are to be centered a hardened bushing a, can be used. c, is a set-screw to keep the work from turning. The set-screw is not tight, however, on the work.

Fig. 41 gives an idea of a small tool used for holding a hair-spring-stud while pinning the spring. The disc *a*, when turned binds the work in the split disc *b*, the stud being held in the center. The elevation shows a section of *a*, which swivels on a bevel-headed screw.

It will be seen that many of the fixtures shown in these figures, though used for small work, will apply equally well to larger operations.

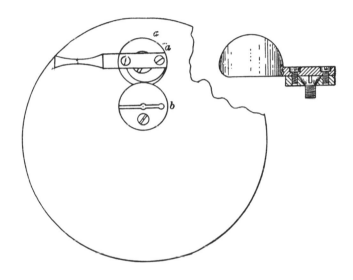

FIG. 41.

Fig. 42 is a plain binding device, which can be swung around or made to slide back as shown in the cut. A holder like this secures the work firmly, and where not used frequently is practical and effective.

It has proved very expensive, however, when used thousands of times in succession, where but little power is required. Many pieces of work that require to be clamped are located by pins or studs, and it should be the aim to do this when possible. The resistance against the cutter is taken in this way by the pins, and the clamp or binder s only required to hold the work down.

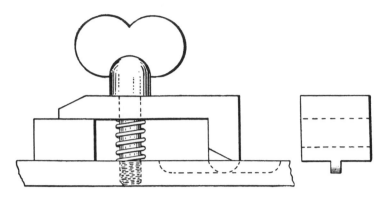

FIG. 42.

In Fig. 42 the spiral spring lifts the clamp from the
work as soon as released by the thumb-screw.

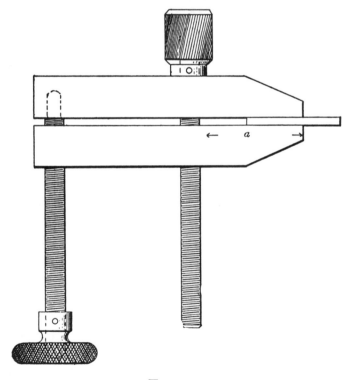

FIG. 43.

In many places a simple bow-shaped flat spring swivel-
ing upon a screw is all that is required to hold the work in

position, where the strain comes upon pins in the tool or the work. The great desideratum where work is done by the piece, or where an operation is repeated continually, is in making motions as simple and few as possible. One movement, that would seem insignificant when made but once or twice, becomes quite important when made thousands of times.

This is one of the primary considerations to be kept in mind when making tools or machinery for producing large numbers of one kind of work.

Fig. 43 shows a pair of common clamps, in which the distance a, can be doubled and still make a strong binder. The screws can also be lengthened, which will secure quite a compass for light work. A simple way to make the screws for this clamp is shown in the cut, any convenient size of wire being threaded with die-plate and pinned into knurled brass heads; the smallest being nearest the work.

Where it is required to file a templet, die, or similar work up to an outline; the work can be held horizontally in the clamp as shown; the latter being held in the bench-vise in the position seen. In this way a person can use an eye-glass directly over the work and file close to a line. It is very convenient sometimes to hold work in a handvise in the same way, putting the latter in the bench-vise.

Fig. 44 shows how an appliance may be made to operate effectively and quickly; and also illustrates the advantage of adapting common sizes of material, where practical, instead of using special forgings. Suppose a cut to be made with a milling machine at a, in the top view or plan of the tool. Then b, is made of some regular size square steel. In the elevation, c, which is not shown in the plan, is made of some common size stock, and the other pieces are made of standard size wire, or drill-rod. When d, is released from e, it reaches the pin f, and lifts c, but one motion being required to accomplish the work, in either fastening or loosening the piece to be cut. The pins g, and h, locate the piece to be milled. The screw i, is for adjusting d, if needed.

In connection with this thought of using material judiciously a number of suggestions might be made. It is a good plan in makng a model for a machine that is to be manufactured in quantities to limit the screws and round work in it to as few sizes as possible. Also in any machine shop use screws, dowel-pins, wire, etc., in as limited a variety as consistent with good work.

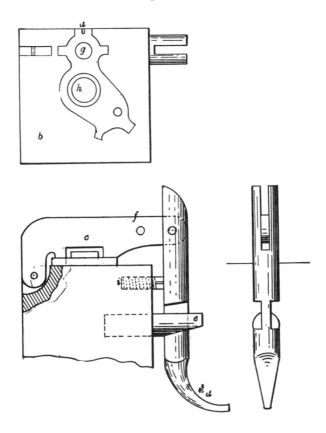

FIG. 44.

Again, it is sometimes cheaper to save on labor than material. For instance, if a great many, or few, for that matter, small running shafts are to be used, as in the counter-hangers in a watch-factory, it will be more profitable to use crescent drill-rod of accurate size, than to turn up tough Bessemer steel.

In using drill-rod for shafting the writer has made a practice of using two sizes, say, .348 in diameter, first, and .358 to follow.   That is, the small size is used until worn too loose, then the counter is reamed out for the larger size rod, and so easily repaired.   In this way the drill-rod is not impaired in quality, but can be used afterwards for the finest tools—drills, taps, reamers etc.

Keep informed as to material and supplies kept in stock by the dealers and adapt such whenever possible to work. It has been the practice of some builders to employ odd

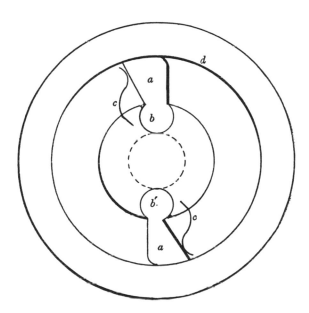

FIG. 45.

threaded screws etc. in their productions, with a view to securing repairs and furnishing supplies in their particular line, but such a practice generally recoils on the author in the long run.

It is said that one of the largest watch-factories in the country meets its pay-roll with the receipts from the sale of repair material.

And a jeweler writing from a southern city some years ago, claimed that the cheapest way to secure such material was to buy a cheap grade of watches and dissect them for that purpose.

Fig. 45 is an illustration of a simple and effective clutch. a, a', swivel at b, b', and are kept in position by the springs c, c, binding on the rim d.   This clutch works very nicely.

Quite a volume might be written and illustrated on this subject, but the limits of this small work will not admit of it here.

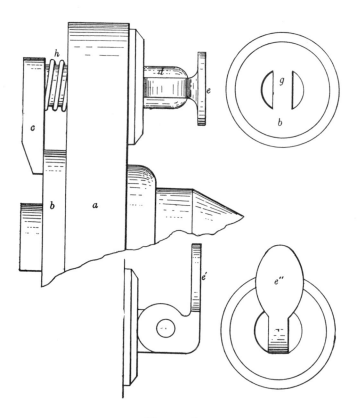

FIG. 46.

Good working samples of different kinds of clutches can be seen in the "Star", and other bicycles; and in the variety of engine-lathe drivers now in use.

Fig. 46. Let a, show a face-plate chuck on lathe, and b, a piece of work fastened to same. c, is a clamp on a stud d, running clear through a. e, e', e'', is a cam with handle which serves to turn *d*, around, also to tighten the binder *c*. The washer or seat for the cam is seen at *f*. The strip *g*, in the center is left solid, and the stud *d*, being split, straddles this, and lets the cam *e*, work on *g*. When *e*, is lifted it loosens *c*, which is raised from the work by the spiral spring *h*. Then by turning *e*, the cam *c*, is swung away from *b*.

This makes a cheap and good chuck for cuts in watch-plates etc., or work held in position by pins.

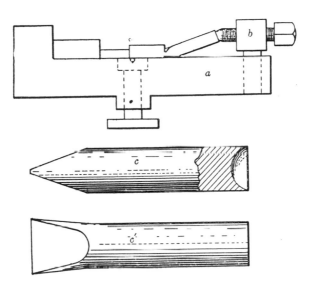

FIG. 47.

Fig. 47 is one of the most useful tools found about a planer. A casting *a*, of any desired length is fitted to the planer, and holes drilled in it for receiving studs like *b*. These are furnished with set-screws and pins *c*, *c'*, of different lengths, and of the shape shown in the cut. Long thin strips of work, such as gibs for slide-rests can be held in the manner shown and not sprung in the least. It requires but a very slight pressure from the screws to hold the work very firmly with this device. The cut represents an end view of the casting.

Fig. 48, illustrates a little tool for holding work, that
may find an application in some other place than the one
shown in the cut.   In this instance a barrel-bridge to a
watch is held in position for damas-keening. It is a piece
of work difficult to hold in any other way, as the whole
surface has to be finished.   It is also quite thin, beveled
on the edges, and cut out on the under side in places.
There are two holes in the bridge *a*, which are located on
the pins *b*, *b*.   All the bridges have holes punched in the

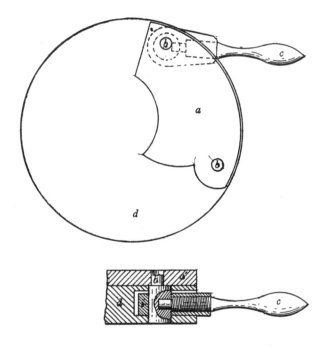

FIG. 48.

same position.   One of the pins *b*, is stationary while the
other *b'*, as shown in the sectional view is movable.   The
later is eccentric to its body as shown in the cuts; which
is driven through *d*, and *i*, after which the handle *c*, is
screwed into *i*, with its point entering the pin *b'*.

This pin tightens in one position and holds the bridge
firmly, without effecting its position perceptibly.

Fig. 48A interprets itself. *a*, is a pin or stud passing

through a split piece *b*, *b*, and collar *c*. *d*, is a handle passing through both collar and pin.   The collar has a winding cam or portion of a screw-thread climbing upon the
hardened pin *e*, to close the ends *b*, *b*.

Eccentric pins or studs make very powerful binders,
and are used for lathe-heads and tail-stocks, swivel tool-
posts, or slide–rests, and other fixtures too numerous to

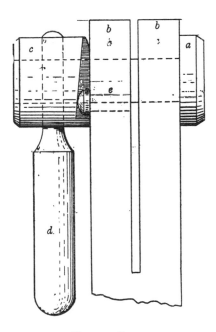

FIG. 48A.

mention. They are notably useful in closing glass moulds,
and securing a good joint.

Fig. 33. In connection with this figure it might have
been mentioned, that the screw and pin for binding make
a good substitute for check-nut 'or washer as used on ball
bearings in bicyles.   A brass plug threaded can be forced
directly against the thread of the nut to be held, or where
the nut runs on a thin shell with spindle or arbor inside
the pin, can be pushed against the inside of the shell tightening the nut, the shell having a tongue made by sawing
into it end-ways twice.

V.

THE MODERN BENCH-LATHE.

The origin of what is known as the Whitcomb lathe seems to be a controverted point, both Mr. Ambrose Webster, and Mr. Geo. F. Ballou claiming to have designed the same. In the catalogue of the American Watch Tool Co., of Waltham Mass., of 1890, it is claimed that Mr. Webster developed the 3° and 45° angle lathe spindle through several stages, designing the same, and perfecting a method of grinding the hardened spindle and bushings.

In the catalogue of the Ballou Manufacturing Co., Hartford, Conn. of 1885, it is said that Mr. Ballou designed the Whitcomb lathe throughout.

Be that as it may, this style of bench-lathe is certainly a great acquisition to the list of modern fine tools. The lathe as illustrated in these cuts, one-third actual size, is made of standard quality throughout by the American Watch Tool Co. Waltham, Mass.

Other makers furnish the same style of tool with some variations in details: two dealers at least, viz: The Hinckley Mfg., Co., of Aurora, Ill., and Sloan, Chace & Co., of Newark, N. J.

It seems that in 1872, Messrs. John E. Whitcomb and Geo. F. Ballou formed a copartnership and commenced the manufacture of this kind of lathe. In 1874, Mr. Ballou retired, and in 1876 Mr. Webster joined Mr. Whitcomb and the company has since been known as the American Watch Tool Co.

In 1885, judging from this catalogue, Mr. Ballou superintended The Ballou Mfg., Co., of Hartford, Conn., and brought out some other fine designs of lathes, and other tools, which seem to establish his title to rare ability in that line of work. His universal watchmakers' lathe, bench-lathe, and engine-lathe fully attesting the above.

Since then the business has passed into the hands of The Dwight Slate Machine Co., of Hartford, Conn., who

hold the Ballou invention and make the tools of his design.

Smaller lathes of the same style, especially for jewellers
use, are made by Mr. Mosely, of Elgin, Ill., and the
Hinckley Mfg., Co., as well as by the American Watch
Tool Co.

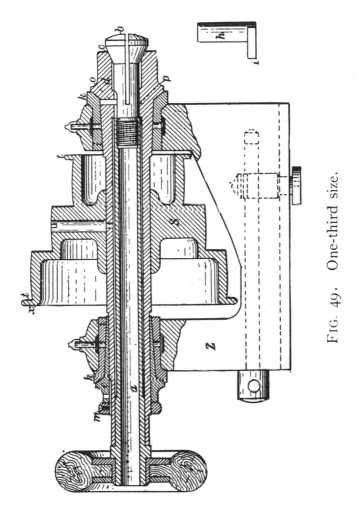

FIG. 49. One-third size.

Having thus mentioned impartially the different makers of this style of lathe, a description of the lathe itself
and its attachments will be in order.

Fig. 49 is a sectional drawing of a headstock to an

American Watch Tool Co's., No. 3, Bench-lathe. The cut is ⅓ actual size and will give a clear idea of the construction of this style of lathe. *a*, is called the draw-in spindle, as its work is to draw the chuck *b*, or other fixture against the angle, *c*, an angle of 40°; or 20° on a side.

The running spindle *d*, is hardened and ground as far back as the bearing surface extends, the angles being 3° and 45°. The back-bearing is a hardened sleeve or shell *e*, with a pin entering a slot in the spindle *d*, which carries it with the latter. The bushings *k*, are also hardened and ground.

The end-shake in the bearing is taken up with the nut *m*; the spindle *d*, being threaded with a fine thread for a short distance at that place.

It was formerly the practice to secure this nut with a set-screw and brass seat, but this method gave place to that of sawing through one side of the nut and closing it up before screwing onto the spindle.

Another plan for tightening a nut was to saw into it in the direction of the threads, or to split it half way through, then to draw the threads together with a screw at right-angle to the threads, passing through one side of the slit and screwing into the other.

o, shows the location of the chuck-pin, which should be made with a head milled or filed like *h*, to fit the slot in the chucks–the tongue *i*, being turned toward the back of the lathe. The pin is inserted from the inside of the spindle.

The portion of the running spindle *d*, shown by the arrow *p*, is known as the throat of the lathe and is a vital point. The chucks should fit perfectly at this place; and in order to provide for any change of size by constant wear it is a good plan to put a hardened bushing in this part of the lathe, which can be replaced at any time. The throat should be left undersize and ground to a standard size after the lathe has been finished and put in running order.

Among the improvements that have been made in the construction of the bench-lathe, is that of lengthening the spindle in front so as to bring the throat pin and the

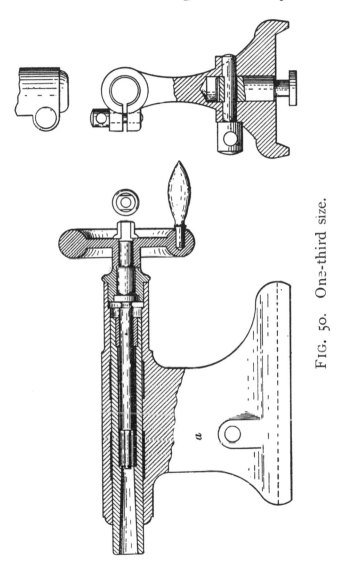

FIG. 50.   One-third size.

throat itself ahead of the 3° and 45° angles, also to length-en the spindle in front of *k*, sufficiently to allow of thread-ing it for heavy chucks and faceplates, taking the strain off of the throat-pin.

Fig. 49, represents the lathe head-stock and the remaining parts need but little description. It will be noticed that the cones of the pulley *s*, are slightly convex to insure the best contact with the belt; and the flanges *t*, prevent the latter from wedging in between the pulley and the frame.

A very convenient, and in fact indispensable feature, not shown in the drawing, consists of an index drilled in the flange at *x*. Two rows of holes are drilled here and a pawl or adjustable pin is attached to the casting *Z*, to accompany the same

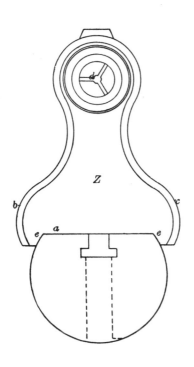

FIG. 51.
One-third size.

The oil-cups are shown in detail in Fig. 53, a wire being used to maintain a flow of oil from the cup into the tube. In Fig. 49, the casting *Z*, is chambered at both ends around the bushings *k*, for oil-wells. Tapering V shaped grooves are cut on the inside of these bushings to carry oil all along the bearings. Several holes are drilled in the bushings, and the V shaped grooves run out before reaching the edges of the same, being deepest at the bend of the angles.

Too much importance cannot be attached to the practice of providing for properly oiling any machine; and a chapter might be written on the different methods of doing the same.

Fig. 50 is a sectional view of the tail-stock, similar in construction to that of most engine-lathes.

The screw is cut with a left-hand thread for convenience, and furnished with a point, as shown in the illustration, for pushing out the taper center as the spindle is drawn back. Circular indices are graduated on collars attached to

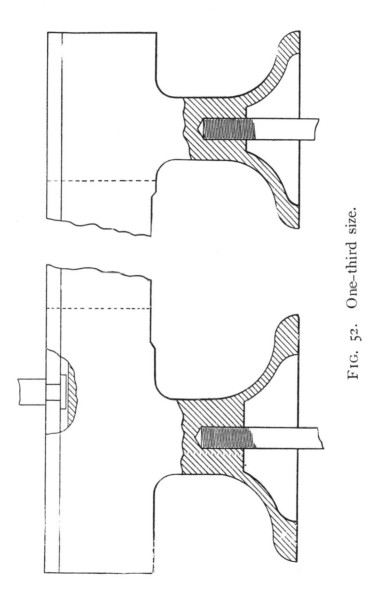

FIG. 52. One-third size.

the screws so as to feed up in hundredths or thousandths, both on the tail-stock and slide-rest. The tail-stock spindle has also a straight scale or index for getting depths

in drilling etc. This would be a good feature on engine-
lathe spindles, and could be put on at any time.

Some of the appliances shown in detail in other figures
are seen applied here. Fig. 51, is an end-view of head-
stock and part of bed, and Fig. 52 shows the bed and ped-
estal as cast in one piece; 28 inches being a good length
for general machine shop purposes.

The face-plates, universal chucks, etc., are attached to
solid chuck-blanks fitting the lathe spindle; and in some
instances the spindle has the projecting end threaded for
carrying the large attachments more firmly.

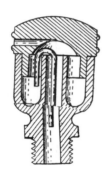

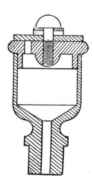

FIG. 53. Full size.   FIG. 54.

The above sketches will furnish good working drawings
for any one who feels like making one of these lathes for
himself. And composition, or even babbitt, will make a
good substitute for the hardened bushings.

In fitting the lathe bearings, the 3° angle must not be
tight, as it binds the lathe spindle upon the least pressure
when the 45° angles are not in full contact.

Before boring out the casting for the bushings *k*, the
surface *a*, on Fig. 51, must be roughed out on the shaper,
leaving enough to finish on the planer. This will avoid
springing the casting, which will be apt to happen if the
scale is not removed until *k*, is bored out. So the steel
spindles should be roughed out nearly to size, and annealed carefully, when the finishing turnings, preparatory to
hardening, are made.

The impression seems to have obtained in many shops that the above described lathe is a kind of toy-machine; but such a thought is usually dispelled after using one, and followed by a sense of surprise at having done so long without it.

The spindle is very easy running, long between the bearings, and the work being held close to the head, makes the lathe much stiffer than many others larger but differently constructed. When equipped with a good supply of wire and step-chucks its convenience cannot be estimated until used.

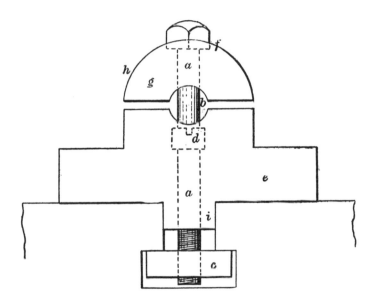

FIG. 55.   Half size.

An idea of the counter hangers, grinder attachments, etc., belonging to the lathe can be obtained readily from the catalogues published by the different makers.

Since the method of lining the head and tail-stock involves an excellent principle of doing this kind of work a description of the same will be inserted here.

Fig. 55.   In this figure we have an end view of a fixture for the planer, 2¼ inches long, with the double bolt a, a, in the center.   This will make the shape of the piece

sufficiently clear without further drawings. The profile
seen in this view is continuous throughout the piece.

It may be desirable to plane up four lathes at a time, so
it is well to make nine pieces like Fig.55. This will provide
for holding eight castings, four headstocks, and four tail-
stocks. Other tools than lathes can be lined up in the
same way. Suppose that a headstock like Z, Fig. 49, is to
be lined up or planed true with a, Fig. 50, the tailstock
for the same lathe. The part to be planed is shown at a,
Fig. 51. Now it will be seen on Fig. 57 that different
sized arbors are provided for different sized borings. But

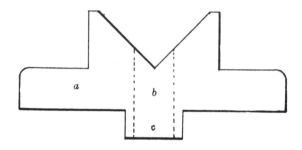

FIG. 56.   Half size.

each arbor is furnished with ends exactly alike, and like
the ends on all the others used in connection with Fig. 55.

In Fig. 57, a, for example, may be an arbor for the
casting Z, in Fig. 49, and the body of the arbor will fit the
borings that receive the bushings k; while a similar arbor
of smaller diameter will fit the casting a, Fig. 50, at the
borings for the spindle.

The ends of the arbors being $^6/_{10}$ in diameter will fit the
circle b, on Fig. 55, at which place they are clamped. Fig.
55 must have the end of a $^6/_{10}$ arbor at each end, or a $^6/_{10}$
plug at one end so that the binding screw a, will pinch the
arbors. a, Fig. 55 is screwed into the planer nut c, by
means of a hollow screw-driver whose points enter opposite slots like the one shown at d. This draws the block e,
down to the planer bed, after which the nut f, binds the
arbors.

Fig. 58 illustrates a brace or support for the castings while being planed. The angle-iron a, is placed in the outside T slot of the planer; there being one for each size of the work; the clamp shown in Fig. 55 being in the middle slot. The screw b, Fig. 58, touches the casting Z, Fig. 51, at b, holding it against a similar screw at c, on the opposite side. Fig. 59 gives a detail drawing of c, Fig. 58. This piece admits of a wide range of adjustment. A standard or templet corresponding to the form at a, Fig. 51, is placed in line with the work on the planer, which is al-

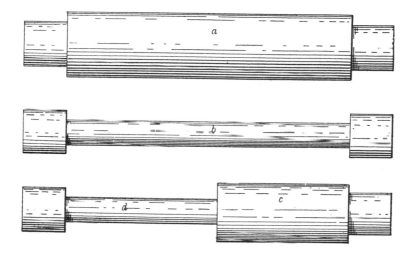

Fig. 57.

ways used to set the planing tool for the height of a, from the center d, and the width between angles e, e.

This makes the parts of different lathes interchangeable as well as coincident between the particular set on the planer at one time.

In Fig. 57 it will be seen that on a, the body of the arbor is larger than the ends, which admits of turning the latter on the arbor, while in b, the ends have to be filled out to size with sleeves or rings. c, d, is an arbor adapted to a casting with a large bore at one end and a small one at the other, similar to some step-lathes. Returning to Fig. 55, it is quite important to make this clamp, or the series of clamps just right; and it may be done in the following way:

The block *e*, and *g*, are cast in one piece to start with and an arm not shown in the cut is cast near *h*, on either side. Then the $^6/_{10}$ hole *b*, is made, being reamed out and ground with a lead arbor to a standard size.

A set of blocks like *a*, Fig. 56, nine in number is made; the angle being 90, in planing which the planer tool is set in one position for the last cut, and the blocks are all

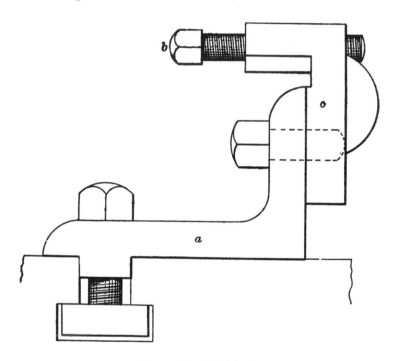

FIG. 58.   Half size.

turned around and planed with the tool in this position which brings the 90° perfectly central with the tongue *c*. A straight hole for bolts like *b*, passes through these; and the series of clamps shown in Fig. 55 are held on arbors clamped on these V blocks and planed all at once. The clamps are located to plane the tongue *i*, central with the hole *b*, by means of the arms mentioned as being cast at *h*. This is clamped to the planer bed while one side of

tongue is planed.   Then the castings are reversed in the
V's and the arms h, are clamped to the planer bed on the
opposite side and the planer tool in same position makes a
cut.   Now having the tongue planed central, and a small
amount of stock to be removed on the last cut, so that they
will enter the planer slot, measure with micrometer, and
find say $4/1000$ to plane off.   Then plane carefully until the
width is reduced $2/1000$, reverse the V's again, and fasten by
the arm and plane opposite sides of tongue without moving the planer tool sideways.

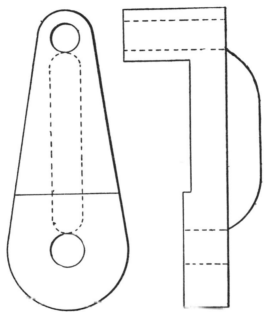

FIG. 59.   Half size.

It might be asked, why not use these V blocks right
along in the place of the ones with the $6/10$ holes? Because,
the line of the contact for the ends of the arbors would be
so small that the pressure required to hold the work,
would injure both the arbors and the V's, and throw the
work out of line in a very brief time.

It will be seen that a set of these clamps once prepared
will cover a wide range of work, and secure at once an
absolute degree of accuracy, admitting at the same time

with the use of templets or guides, of duplicating nice work when desirable.

Fig. 49 again. Having disposed of the casting Z, let us consider the hardened spindle and bushings. First, however, attention should be called to the fact that the casting Z, has been faced off when k, is pressed in. A projection must be cast here and left until turned on centers and used for back-resting to bore out the holes for k, after which they can be turned off on an arbor.

Another advantage, and one which should be provided for in casting, where it is desired to secure a nice hole ground with lead arbor to exact size the whole length, is obtained in this way: that is, by leaving stock to cut off at the ends, after grinding the holes to size, the effect of making the holes bell-muzzled or largest at the ends is remedied. The lead-arbor is almost certain to do this.

Having rough-turned, annealed, turned to size proper for grinding, and hardened, the spindle and bushings are ready to grind and stone to a bearing. Remember to put in all oil holes, etc., before hardening. It is a good practice to mill a little slot in the end of both bushings at i, not shown in cut, and to put a pin or set a screw in the casting here to enter the same, to prevent the bushings turning around if not forced in very tight.

After hardening, the pieces are heated *at once* until solder will melt when placed against them, and left at this temper. The amount left for grinding depends on the shape of the piece, its tendency to spring in hardening, and the chances of straightening it afterwards, etc. This spindle only requires hardening at the bearing. Straight spindles that have sprung in hardening can frequently be straightened by placing in a vise between three pins two on one side and one on the other; and compressing after heating with a spirit lamp or bunsen burner until saliva will hiss upon them. When sprung as far as felt to be safe they must be allowed to cool in this position. There is risk of breaking of course, but it is sometimes preferable to re-hardening.

The bushings *k*, are secured to a brass chuck with solder, or true split chuck true with outside and both angles nicely ground. *e*, is ground out with lead arbor to fit spindle *d*.

A disc is soldered into the end of spindle *d*, at *c*; the spindle backrested over the throat *p*, and a good center made in the disc. The 3° 45° angles are then ground, seeing that they coincide with 3° angle on *k*, grinding until the two 45° on *d*, and *k*, hold a piece of tissue paper. Grind *e*, on the spindle the same way. A slip of Washita oil-stone five or six inches long by one inch square is very convenient to stone off the spindle and bearing *e*, until they run smoothly in *k*, *k*. Be sure that the 3° angle bearing is not tight as it locks the lathe upon the least pressure on the center.

Having stoned to a nice fit, *k*, *k*, are held in position on the spindle with spiral spring between them and ground outside on the spindle centers to press into the head *Z*.

Afterwards the throat *p*, and bearing for chuck at *c*., are ground after the lathe is running.

The Ballou universal engine lathe is a bench lathe with many excellent features. The head and tailstock are overhanging. The slide-rest has an up and down or vertical adjustment. It has two screws, one a precision screw for cutting nice threads to perfection. The screw for general use has a novel and useful feature. The carriage is moved when desired by the screw, working on a worm gear, which being fast, takes the place of the ordinary lead-screw nut and can be used as a pinion or wheel working in a rack: the screw being confined in its position when standing still becomes the rack, and the worm gear being disengaged travels upon it, carrying the carriage rapidly by hand. In this way the lathe carriage can be used for long accurate grinding, making a good substitute for a parallel grinder.

Bench lathes like those described, once introduced, generally become indispensable; and a shop is incomplete in its equipment at this time without one or more.

The practice prevalent in most shops of making small screws, dowel-pins, etc., with a hand graver, and a drill-chuck used in the speed lathe, the work sticking out four or five inches from the lathe-bearing, is a reflection on the intelligence of the managers of such places.

An Almond drill-chuck fitted to a taper and used in the engine lathe is a great improvement on this; but unless used carefully is soon a wreck, and at the best a poor caricature on a good bench lathe.

The author makes the above plea for the bench lathe, knowing that every first class mechanic who has ever used one will gladly approve of such a mention; especially when trying to do a fine job in some old drill-lathe with egg-shaped bearings, that run like a bottle in a horse collar.

VI.

CHUCKS OF DIFFERENT KINDS.

Following in natural order a description of the bench-lathe is that of the chucks accompanying it.

Fig. 60 gives the actual size of four chucks corresponding in number to a series of lathes that are used in the Aurora Watch factory;—No. 4 being the size used in the machine department bench-lathe.

They are called solid or split chucks, according as they enter the lathe whole, as shown in Fig. 60, or as sawed in three places to permit the angle of lathe resting upon angle of chuck at *a*, Fig. 60, to close the same under pressure.

A chuck-blank like No. 4 with taper projection should be fitted up with an Almond drill-chuck for twist drills.

Fig. 61 shows an attachment to lathe spindle for use in closing larger chucks. *a*, is the end of a three-bearing lathe spindle, and *b*, represents a chuck of ordinary size for No. 4 lathe. *c*, is a hardened and ground ring used with spindle a, when a split-chuck with large face is to be used.

In Fig. 61 such a chuck is shown by the dotted lines—the pressure coming at d.

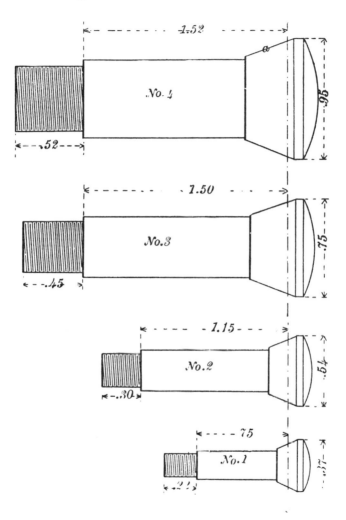

FIG. 60.

In Fig. 62, the face of such a chuck is shown; and it can be seen with what facility a similar cut can be made in several pieces at the same time. The chuck is sawed at a, a, a, after the piece b, is screwed into proper position.

The cut is made in this case at c, c, c, the pieces, which are barrel bridges to a watch being sunk about half their depth into the piece b, made three pieces by sawing at a, a, a.

What is known as a three-bearing lathe is one so arranged that the spindle a, Fig. 61, is pushed up against the chuck b, or d, to close it, instead of having the chuck

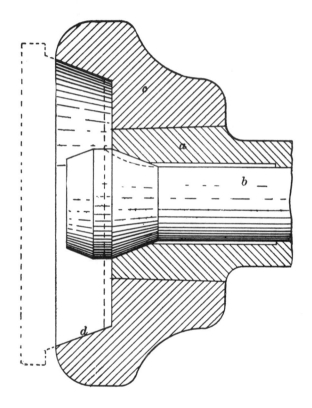

FIG. 61.

drawn back against the spindle as in a two-bearing lathe. In the first instance the chuck, in the second the spindle, being stationary.

Where the chuck is drawn into the lathe a variation in the pressure applied to close the same will affect the position of the work more or less; and while the cutter may be accurately gauged the depth of the cut in different pieces will vary accordingly. This is remedied by forcing the spindle up against the chuck, as the work always comes the same horizontally.

Fig. 63. This chuck was substituted by the writer in the place of an eccentric split chuck, which always proved a source of trouble. This one has been in use for years without losing any of its efficiency.

It is used for turning brass pottances, and as shown is subjected to a heavy strain. The first diameter of the pottance

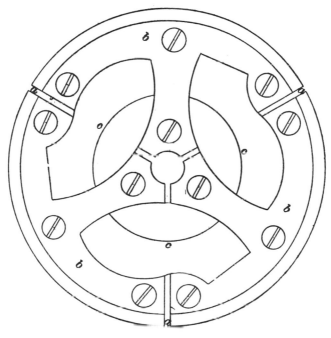

FIG. 62.

is shown by dotted line at *a*. After turning the projection *b*, in another chuck, the work is held by the same, and the boss *c*, is cut. The turning diameter is shown at *d*, by dotted lines, and three cuts are made to get the diameter of *c*. It will be seen that the slot *e*, is arranged to catch the work directly where ths resistance to the cutter comes, and the screw *f*, adapted to a socket-wrench, though slower working than a cam, gets the greatest power.

Fig. 64 is a chuck for making a light diameter turning on a brass pillar-plate for a watch, at *a*. This plate is held in position by three pins, not shown in cut, which enter the dial feet holes in the pillar plate. They are fixed in plate *b*, of the chuck.

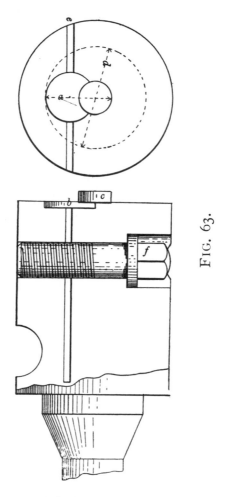

FIG. 63.

The pillar plate is held against the face of the chuck by a snap or spring stop fastened to the lathe-bed. It is a simple flat spring pressing against the work as a person might do with his finger, the pin carrying the plate around. In Fig. 64 the ring *c*, *c'*, has three inclined

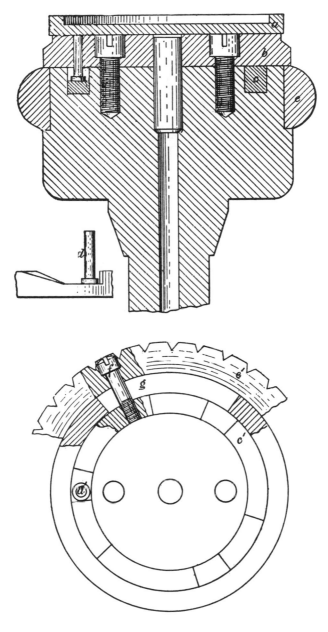

FIG. 64.

planes on its surface, which lift the pins d, d'', to throw the pillar plate off of the chuck-pins when finished.

The outer ring *e*, *e'*, is connected with *c*, *c'*, by screw *f*, and carries the same to limit of slot *g*. When returned the pins push back to place as shown at *d*, Fig 64. The pins in the regulator of a watch are very small and close together, and the holes for receiving them are drilled on

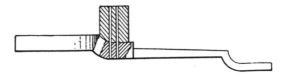

FIG. 64A.

Showing bushing used in Regulator drilling jig.

the curve of the regulator arm. In Fig. 64A, the bushings for guiding the drill is shown on top of the regulator; but in some cases the holes are drilled through the curve.

The bushing is secured in a holder or jig and fitted to the form of the regulator.

The most important point in relation to this work is that of getting the two holes correct in the bushing, which

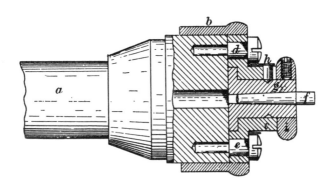

FIG. 65.

is done in the following manner: Fig. 65 is a special chuck for this purpose, and shows a good method for drilling very small holes close together on any occasion.

When the chuck is once located correctly and marked, it can always be used to replace the bushings without any difficulty. It is quite important in constructing tools and machinery to provide for replacing any part that is liable to be soon worn out or broken. Some pieces of a machine may be almost indestructible, while others are unvoidably short lived; and provision must be made for renewing the latter.

In Fig. 65. *a*, is a part of a No. 4, solid chuck, *b*, the outside ring, when in place, makes everything concentric. When this is removed the piece *c*, can be swung on the stationary stud *d*, as the same piece *c*, is slotted at the binding screw *e.*

The required distance for moving this is found by experiment, and when in proper position a delicate line is made upon *a*, and *c*, for locating *c*, again.

A number of taper blanks like *f*, with sufficient length for the bushings are made, and one of the holes is drilled with *c*, eccentric. *g*, is then turned half around, being located by the pawl-pin, held by flat spring. This brings the taper in position for drilling the other hole. *i*, is a ring for turning *g*. This appliance may serve some reader in other ways.

It requires but very little pressure on the pins to hold the work as the holes are so small, and they are started with a smaller graver.

The drill for such small holes is generally soldered into a brass wire and held between the finger and thumb. After a center is made with the graver a small drill held this way will guide itself. It can be held in a little pin-chuck either. The work must run at a very high rate of speed, and the drill held between the finger and thumb admits of the most sensitive pressure. *e*, binds *c*, but *g*, moves freely in *c*, though fitting closely.

Fig. 66, is a cut that almost explains itself, and shows a chuck for holding balances;—the work to be done on them being light. The shell or sleeve *a*, with inclined slots *c*, in connection with pins *i*, binds the work at *e*. The slots, however, should be reversed and made right-handed.

Fig. 67, is a similar chuck upon a taper shank which enters a No. 4 solid chuck in this case.

This was designed to secure power and quick motion at the same time and worked admirably. *a*, is a binding-nut running upon the thread *d*, and was formerly removed every time a balance was turned exposing the threads to grit and dirt. In this chuck it is only loosened, while a

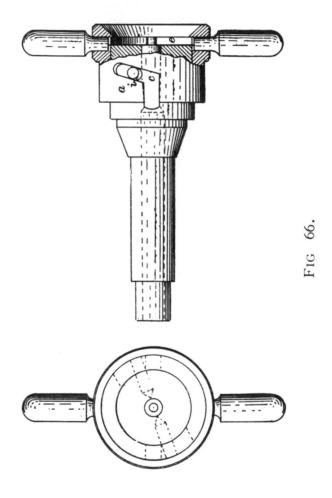

FIG 66.

second clamp-ring *c*, is removed instantly with the work. *c*, shown partly solid and partly in section has two arms or projections which enter right-angled slots in *a*, as shown at *d*, being entered straight and then locked by a partial turn.

When *a*, passes onto the thread it carries *c*, with the projecting arms and tightens the work; and when un-

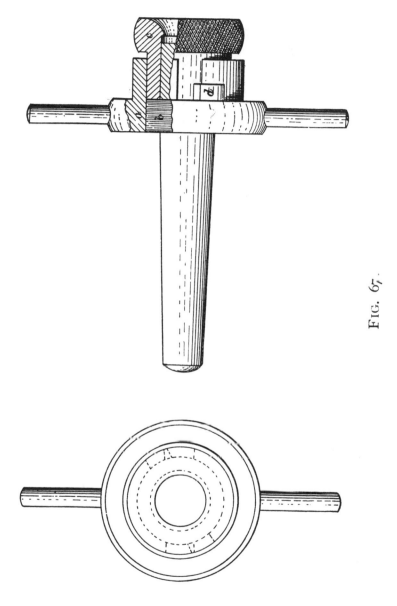

FIG. 67.

screwed it relieves them at once, so that *c*, can be unlocked and taken off.

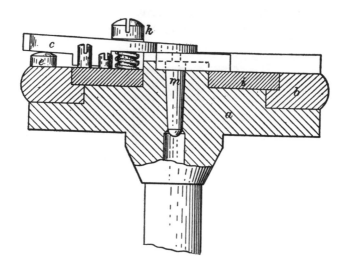

Fig. 68.

Fig. 68, illustrates a principle that has been applied with good results to several different chucks for as many different purposes.

It is a substitute for the thumb-screw way of holding work, and operates quickly and automatically. In this instance the chuck is used for turning the dome for the regulator on the balance-bridge. *a*, is the chuck proper, *b*, is a ring for locking the clamp *c*, *c'*, by means of the

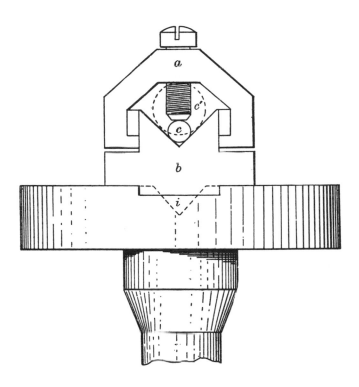

FIG. 69.

stud *d*. The latter carries the clamp onto the pin *e*, *e'*. which does the binding. Before this effect is secured, however, the spring *f*, throws the clamp *c*, *c'*, into position, and then backs further off to allow of *d's*, working.

When the spring *f*, has carried *c*, against the pin *g*, it is in position; and after *d*, and *e*, are removed, the pin *h*.

comes after and unlocks c.   The plate i, holds the ring b, and the stud-screw k, and pin m, centers the work.

Figs. 69 and 70 are an elevation and plan of a very use-ful chuck or face plate; and one which can be used to good advantage on either a large or small lathe.   It is used for boring round work centrally, or as is sometimes required, for threading the ends of two rods.   Pieces threaded this way are sometimes used as seats for set-

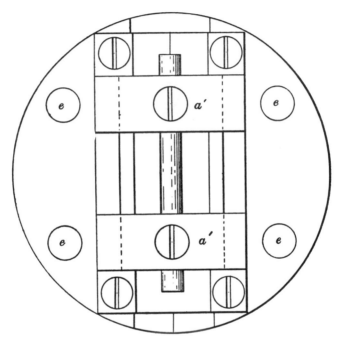

FIG. 70.

screws binding other screws. a, a', are sliding clamps or yokes for holding rods, or round work, as shown by whole and dotted lines c, c'.

If it is desired to hold larger pieces, longer screws can be used in the holes at e, e, e, e, with longer clamps or straps reaching across the V shaped holder b.   The V must be perfectly central.

The dotted lines at s, show a simpler and cheaper plan that will answer very well.   A plain face-plate with a V in the center, and numerous screw or bolt holes for a pair of common clamps to be used with blocks of wood is all that is needed.

Fig. 71 gives a method for turning a perfect sphere or ball. The ball is held in any convenient way for rough-

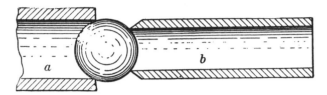

FIG. 71.

ing out, and then held by friction in a hollow cylinder running perfectly true, like *a*. The cutter or turning tool is another true cylinder with sharp edge which is worked over the ball as it revolves with *a*. The ball is shifted in *a*, several times until all the irregularities are removed. It can be used then for a ball joint by drilling hole in it to receive a rod.

Billiard balls are revolved between two discs running in opposite directions while a ring-shaped cutter operates between them.

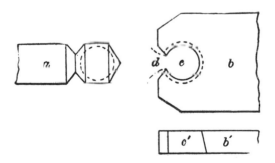

FIG. 72.

Perfectly true hardened balls of uniform size are made now by a patent process, for the ball-bearings in bicycles, etc., and run in several sizes, $^3/_{16}$, $^1/_4$, and $^5/_{16}$ at least.

Fig. 72 illustrates a quick and correct plan for getting

a ball on the end of a rod for a ball-joint. Rough the rod out on the end as shown by whole lines at *a*, then force the tool *b*, over the same while *a*, is revolving in the lathe,

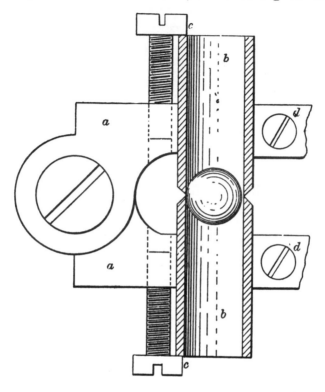

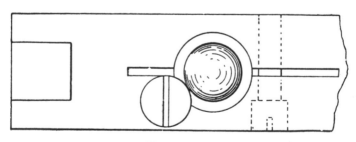

FIG. 73.

which will give the ball end shown by the dotted lines. The hole *c'*, in *b'*, is drilled and reamed out tapering, and then filed open at d, the opening being filed back to cut. The top of c, is stoned smooth for the cutting edge. The diameter of c, will of course regulate the size of the ball.

A ball made the same way with teeth cut on it for shaping the socket can be used for that purpose.

Fig. 73 shows an appliance used for making ball-shaped ends on castings used for treadle rods on some of the sewing machines.

This tool makes the work sufficiently accurate for ordinary purposes. a, a, is a jointed tong or holder with handles of convenient length, eight or ten inches; b, b, are the cutters, being hollow steel cylinders hardened and tempered. c, c, are adjusting screws for the cutters, which also hold them to the work, and d, d, are binding screws for closing the slots e, to hold the cutters. This is a tested tool that works well. The ball revolves while the tool is held in the hand.

Fig. 74 is a picture of an indispensable tool or adjunct to the bench lathe. It is a holder for chucks and in the drawing is one-half the size of same for No. 4 lathe chucks. It is adapted to holding chucks as shown, when either the chuck itself or work held in either solid or split chucks can be handled to advantage.

Suppose it is required to bore an eccentric chuck at d, then the holder can be put on the lathe face-plate at any position and fastened, when the chuck can be readily bored as desired.

Or it may be required to do some irregular milling or planing on a piece of work soldered up on a lathe-chuck, in connection with a turning operation. The chuck with the work mounted can be transferred from the lathe to the milling machine or shaper bed for the purpose, and returned at will. Punches can be milled in this way while the operator looks down on the outline of the work. b, is a nut for drawing the chuck into the holder a, while c, is the plate or base for clamps to rest on.

One or more steel chucks for holding brass blanks should accompany every lathe. A No. 4 chuck blank one inch in diameter with a threaded end one-half inch long by one-half inch in diameter, with fourteen threads

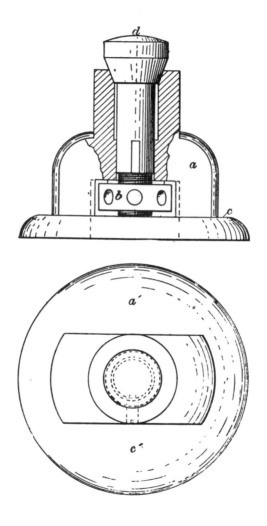

FIG. 74.   Half size.

to the inch, will do. Any number and size of brass blanks can be fitted to these with spanner provided, and kept on hand for soldering work onto.

For absolutely correct work, or making one turning positively true with another made separately from the one to be made, it is essential to have a true face and diameter turning for the work to be fastened to, either by soldering, shellacing, or screwing or clamping in some way.

It will not do to take the work out of the lathe and put it back again in this case. But for all practical purposes, work soldered onto a brass blank can be removed with the blank, for convenience, and another blank put on; or better still where a number of chucks are used, the whole thing can be laid away, while the lathe is used for something else.

In watch making where great accuracy is required a tool named a quill is used extensively for making the cuts and holes in the plate. It consists of a shell made of steel or cast iron as the case demands, with spindle and bearings like those in a lathe. Each quill is finished with a chuck for holding the work, having the particular cut or hole to be made in the plate concentric with the spindle of the quill, and the center of the lathe. A lathe-bed with quill-holder, and simple driving spindle is used, and the quills are located in this way at the height of the regular lathe-spindle so that the slide rests belonging to it can be used. Each part of the work is in this way furnished with its special quill and chuck that are used for that work alone, thus insuring positive accuracy.

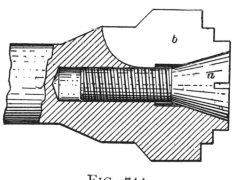

FIG. 74A.

Another and important class of chucks that can be described without any special cuts is the expansion.

These are split chucks that expand to hold the work instead of closing in on it. They are operated with a spindle or rod similar to that shown in Figs. 21 and 22, having a tapering point, which expands

the chuck, the latter being accommodated to the work in
hand. Fig. 74A, gives a cheap chuck of this kind ex-
panded with a bevel head screw a. This chuck can be
made of cast iron and split in three places like b.

A set of step-chucks are of value also. These are chucks
having steps or sinks, of different diameters, several in one
chuck, turned in them, so that all the sinks in a number
of chucks cover any diameter from one-half to two inches.
They can be made of machinery steel or malleable iron,
not requiring to be hardened. A split-chuck of this kind
can spring in closing together two and one-half one hundredths so that that difference can measure the distance
between the diameters of the different steps.

The more steps there are put into one chuck the fewer
will be the chucks required, but the shallower they will be
as the chucks must not project far from the ends of lathe-
spindle. So if the best result is desirable two sinks in each
chuck about one-eight of an inch deep will be a good division. This will allow the chuck to get a good contact
with the work and hold it firmly.

For work above two inches in diameter that cannot be
done in an engine-lathe to good advantage, soldering
chucks of brass can be used profitably.

Since hardened spring chucks are the principal feature
of the bench lathe it may be of interest to know how they
are made. The chucks made by the Hinckley Manufacturing Company, of Aurora, Ill., are of the best Crescent
annealed steel and finely tempered. The work throughout is done with exceptional care as the writer can certify
from observation. The rough work is done either in an
engine or a turret lathe, and requires no description. Sets
of standard plugs and reamers are provided, and after being sawed the chucks are ground out with diamond laps to
accurate size.

As the sawing and grinding outside are the most inter-
esting operations these will be described.

Fig. 75 shows a fixture for this purpose used with a Gar-
vin Universal milling machine. It can be made for any

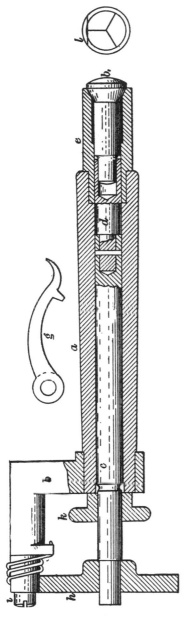

FIG. 75.

milling machine of the same style. *a*, is a hollow tapering spindle that fits the universal head of machine. *b*, is a chuck to be sawed or split as shown in end view. *c*, is a drawing up spindle with extensions at *d*, made in this way for adapting to different sizes of chucks.

The spindle *a*, has an extension piece also, as shown at *e*, for the same reason. This one screws in, the former being pinned in as shown.

The piece *f*, is a pawl frame for holding a pawl similiar to *g*, which works on the index plate *h*, at *i*,—the spring holding it down. *k*, is a binding nut. The piece *e*, is flattened on top and sawed into the required length to saw the chucks.

There is no throat-pin in this spindle, but the slot in the same is sawed up far enough to allow of inserting a slip of metal of any kind into the throat-pin groove in the chuck, it being held in this way until the drawing up spindle is screwed onto the chuck fast by means of the index plate *h*, the pawl being lifted out at the time. After this is done the chuck is located by the pawl entering one of the three cuts in the index plate *h*, when it is tightened in position with the nut *k*. One of the slots in the chuck is then sawed, after which *k*, is loosened and the pawl dropped into the next notch in the index plate. The chuck is

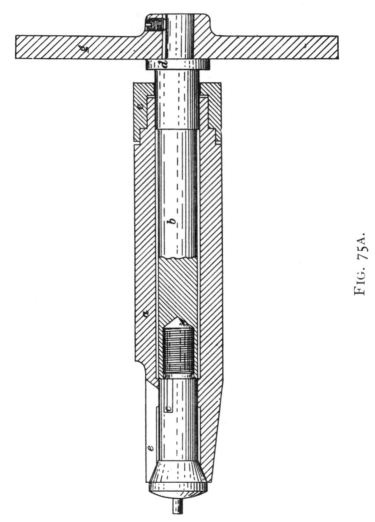

FIG. 75A.

tightened again with *k*, and the next slot sawed. The three slots are cut in this way, the chuck being revolved in the large spindle.

This holder, however, is used only for sawing large chucks

as the regular work for jewellers' trade is done in a small bench milling machine much faster. The same style of holder is used, the saw, however, moving vertically instead of horizontally.

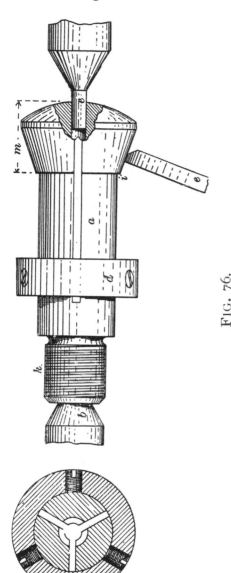

FIG. 76.

This holder as shown in Fig 75 is of inestimable value in connection with the universal milling machine for many other uses. It can be seen readliy that by removing the pawl, and fastening the chuck as before with h, that any kind of work can be held in a split or solid chuck by tightening k, when the whole fixture becomes practically a part of the milling machine head, and the regular operation of that part with its revolving spindle can be applied to the work in the chuck. In this way for instance a disc can be turned up true in a bench lathe, on a solder chuck, and transferred to the milling machine head, where it can be graduated if desired, or milled any way.

Fig. 75A, is a quill or holder for the same purpose as Fig. 75. It is held in a special holder on the milling ma-

chine, and the pawl used with it is held in the **T** slot of
the same.   The chuck is first drawn up as in Fig. 75, and
then tightened in the quill by running the nut c, back
against d.   Step chucks for jewellers' use are sawed in a
quill with a yoke rest.   The chucks are one inch in diameter with many short steps.   They are held in another step
chuck with yoke center in small end of chuck being sawed.   The saw enters the slots in the holding chuck, and
cuts up against the steps of chuck being sawed.

Fig. 76, gives an idea of the way a chuck is ground.   After having hardened and tempered it to a distance shown
by m, the angle surface must be ground true with the hole
at c.   Let e, represent the edge of an emery-wheel running
in opposite direction to the chuck.   That is the chuck
turns down at the point where the emery-wheel touches it,
and the emery-wheel runs up.   This is the principle of
all that class of grinding where the work and grinding-
wheel both revolve, work and wheel running oppositely.

The emery-wheel in this instance is attached to a small
straight hardened spindle running in hardened bushings,
in a casting adapted to the bench lathe slide-rest.   A
light spindle and wheel is preferable to a heavy fixture as
it is more sensitive, and easily kept in repair.   A spindle 5
or 6 inches long and ¼ inch in diameter with whirl-knob
on the end is large enough.   Wheels for general use, 3 inches by $1/10$ of an inch thick, are all right. The Richardson-
wheel made by the Waltham Emery Wheel Co., Walth·
am. Mass., 100 and 120 grade of emery.   They are held
between discs on a taper which enter the spindle, and run
6400 revolutions per min.   Wheels from this size down can
be used in the same way.

Very small holes are ground out with steel laps or plugs
charged with diamond grains.   They must be run at a
high rate of speed; from 8000 to 10,000 revolutions if under ⅛ of an inch in diameter, or even faster.

A light grinder is preferable every way, as power makes no
count in this kind of work, the pressure on the wheel being
merely f·r contact.   Anything more will glaze the wheel.

In using very small laps for inside work it is hard to tell sometimes whether they are working by the sense of touch;

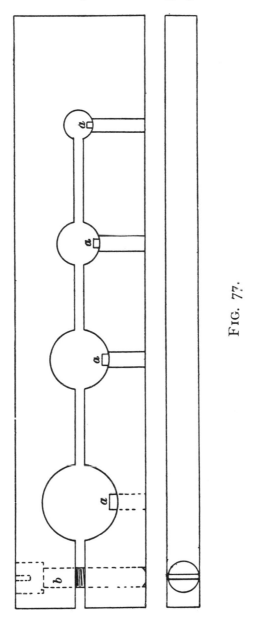

FIG. 77.

but the slightest contact can be distinguished by placing one end of a rod against the front end of the lathe-head, and the other against the bone of the ear.   The end of a screw-driver blade   against   the   lathe, with   the   handle against the base of the ear will communicate the slightest touch of the lap against the work no matter how many sounds besides this are made.

Broken emery or corundum wheels can be utilized for making smaller wheels.   Trim them, after making a hole in the center, with a pair of cutting nippers, and turn to size on the arbor where they are used with a diamond point.   The hole in the center can be drilled with a twist drill run very slow and used with water.   Let the taper or other arbor to which they are fastened have a shoulder, or be roughed up, in some way, and then secure them with hot shellac.

A large emery-wheel can be trued up in the planer in this way.   Run slow as possible.   Finish with wide faced tool, left as hard as fire and water will make it, and feed coarse, using water.

In Fig. 76, d, is a ring with 3 set-screws which holds the divisions of the chuck upon the center c.   These centers

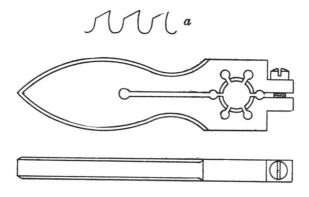

FIG. 78.

are made on tapers which can be changed readily.   The chuck is held against the center b, with a brass back-rest clamp.   A brass driver or dog screws onto k, and a brass yoke pulls it back with the work against the center.   The yoke has two screws passing through the face-plate, with springs between the face-plate and the nuts on the screws, for holding the work against the center *b*. The yoke opens on the side so the chucks can be taken out readily.

Fig. 77, is a holder for the different sized chucks, that is quite convenient. It is held in the hand or vise when a sizing die like that shown in Fig. 78 is run over the threads. Sometimes the threads get marred in some way and need to be run through a die like this. The screw on the end is for adjusting the die as required.

For sawing small chucks a coarse tooth saw is used. A saw $1^1/_{10}$ in. diameter with 28 teeth does good work. The teeth are made for strength, and to sharpen again, like *a*, on Fig. 78.

VII.

SLIDE RESTS AND BENCH-LATHE TOOLS.

Fig. 79. Without giving a complete drawing some of the details of a bench-lathe slide-rest may be shown in this cut, and the one following. A piece called a shoe is fitted to the lathe-bed on the under side, and on the upper side to the bottom of the slide-rest at *a*. A bolt with nut on the lower end passes up through the long opening in the lathe-bed and has a cap shaped head that fills the **T** slot *c*.

Fig. 79. This fastens the slide-rest, **T** rest, etc., to the lathe-bed. *c*, is the screw for the length-feed and has ends of the same size so that the handle can be shifted at convenience. *d, d*, are the two ends of one composition nut attached to the top or tool post slide. Fig. 80 shows another section of the same casting seen in Fig. 79, with the swivel binder which comes to one side of the feed-screw. This is used to tighten the top slide when set for angles.

A later and improved style of slide-rest is made now by the American Watch Tool Co., which in many ways is an improvement on this one, especially for grinding purposes. Fig. 80A is a cut made without regard to size to illustrate an inexpensive nut for a slide-rest screw like that at *c*, Fig. 80. In Fig. 80A *a*, *a'*, is a brass plug driven into the casting and then drilled and tapped for screw to work in

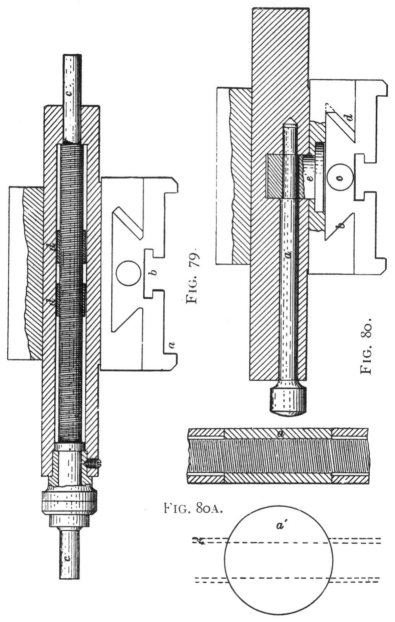

FIG. 79.

FIG. 80.

FIG. 80A.

Other points worth noticing as relating to that class of work in general are the angles of slides such as *b*, and the method of putting in the gibs like a.   The latter is made as shown by the whole rather than the dotted lines.

In this way the gib has a wide bearing surface, and the slide-rest casting is left strong, and it is easily fitted. The gib-screws are beveled on the ends to correspond to the angle of the gib, tending to crowd it up to top of slide. (See. Fig. 86.) The gib has one pin to keep it in position endways.

A lesser angle on these slides would tend to wedge and cause them to run hard.

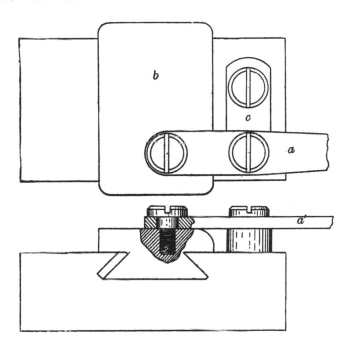

FIG. 81.

In Fig. 81, and following cuts, a number of special features are illustrated without giving any complete drawings of the tools to which they belong. Fig. 81, is a good practical lever for carrying the slide b, a, a', and c, showing its working features. The same result is secured in a model way on some of the turret lathes, where a swivel or revolving post is used with a ball shaped top through which the handle moves as it approaches and recedes with the motion of the slide.

Fig. 82, is another lever in which the handle drops down as it moves the rest back, and lifts up to move it forward. The roller secures a smooth easy motion.

In some places one style is more convenient and in others another.

Fig. 83, illustrates a friction handle to a slide or boring-rest. It is a device that might not be in demand once in a thousand times, but was used at one time in turning out balance-blanks to a uniform depth. Where an ordin-

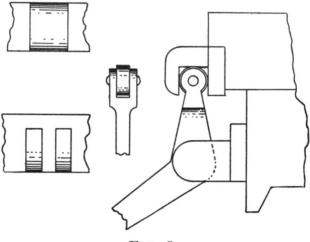

FIG. 82.

ary handle to screw feed is used it can generally be strained and made to go by a stop, but in this case when pushed so hard against a gauge the friction slips and the slide stops. a, a', shows one of three springs which secure the friction. These springs are given the proper tension with the screws b, b', and carry the slide until the stop is touched.

In this way a number of pieces of work can be faced off or bored very accurately as to depth.

Sometimes a slide is made that requires to be moved but a short dsstance and not very frequently; and yet nicely adjusted or set for a permanent job. Fig. 84 shows a cheap and practical way to do this.

a, is a screw that holds a little tongue on the slide which fits a groove in the screw *b*.   In the cut the slide *c*, is as far forward as it can go; but when *b*, is turned back it carries *c*, with it.

Figs. 85, 86, 87, contain several points that may interest the reader.   They represent the two tool carriages to a small screw-lathe and are similar to the larger devices of

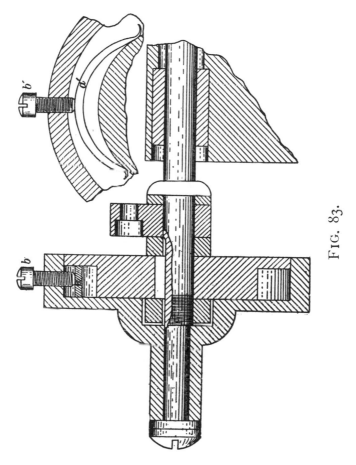

FIG. 83.

the same kind on screw lathe with the turret heads.   *a*, is the clamp for tool, with tongue at *c*, to keep it in place when tightened.   The piece *d*, is fed up or down by the screw *e*, and bound in position with the screw *i*.   *k*, gives a good idea of an ordinary ball joint, or more properly a

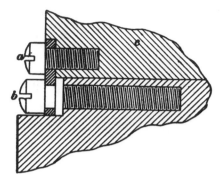

FIG. 84.

toggle. Two yokes like this stand at right angles to each other and the screw points enter the four quarter points of a ring or ball. The feed screw has a collar with pin entering a slot in the screw stem. This prevents its turning around when the check-nut is brought against it and so unscrewing the latter.

The shoulder of a screw is provided with a hardened collar, so that a good plan for taking up the end shake of the screw is furnished. Fig. 85, is a front elevation in re-

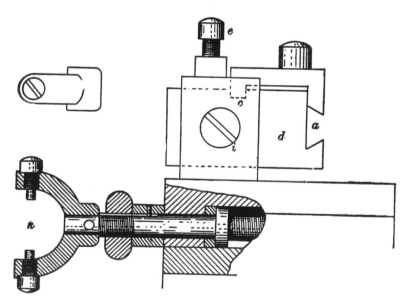

FIG. 85.

lation to the lathe, and Fig. 86 gives an end view of double slide rest.

The casting is adapted, as shown, to the circle of lathe

chuck which projects pretty well.   It will be seen that *a*, is lower than *b*, which happens for the purpose of bringing the cutting edges of the tools nearly opposite.   For the cutter in *b*, cutting on the back side of the work must be put in upside down to meet the upward turn of the piece

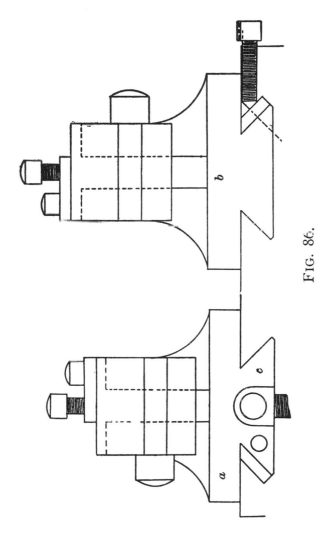

FIG. 86.

in the lathe.   The gib-screw here though larger than needed, shows with the dotted lines, how the pressure comes on the center of the gib in the right direction.

Fig. 87, gives a top view or plan of the above cuts 85 and 86.

c, in Fig. 86 shows a common style of nut for the feed screws in slide-rests where they are not very long. This is an end view of a piece from ⅜ to ½ inch long.

Fig. 88, is still another style of feed-screw nut as shown

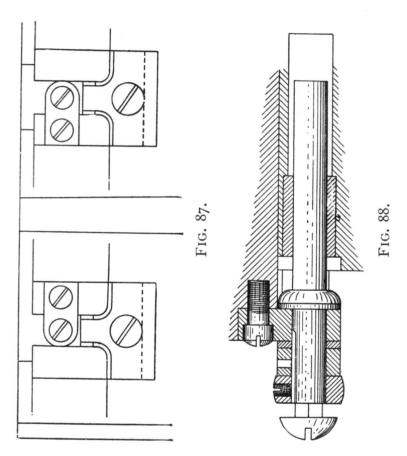

FIG. 87.   FIG. 88.

at *a*. The washers on the screw are arranged a little differently from those in Fig. 85.

Fig. 89, at *a*, shows a nut similar to *c*, in Fig. 86, being held in place with screw *c*, however, in the place of screwing in. *c*, is a stop-screw with a friction piece to keep it from turning. This is held against the screw by the spring, shown better in Fig. 90.

Fig. 91, is a swivel and binder made for the same purpose as *a*, and *e*, in Fig. 80, but more expensive and no
better if as good.

Fig. 92, is a very good slide-rest tool-post where but

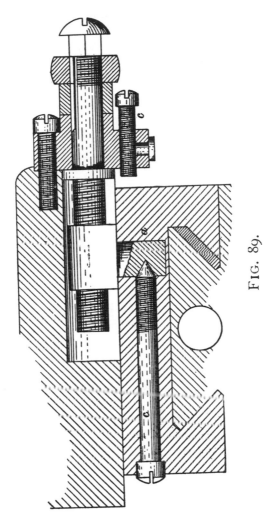

FIG. 89.

little up and down adjustment is required. The two
pieces shown at *a*, are threaded for the purpose of raising
and lowering the tool.

Figs. 93 and 94 are two views of a special slide-rest, the
only thing of general interest about it being the novel

way of holding the cutter, and the shape of the cutter itself. Cutters of this shape are planed up in strips a foot
long and then cut off in short pieces. They only require

FIG. 90.   FIG. 91.

to be ground on top as they are planed up with the proper
pitch to cut well. a, is an end view of the cutter, and b, b,

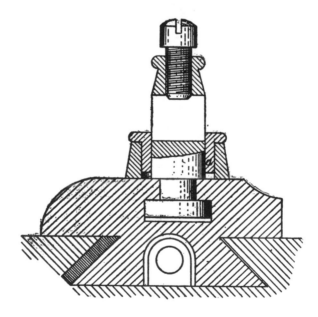

FIG. 92.

is a bolt and binder combined for fastening the tool firmly.   A top view is shown in Fig. 94.

Cutters made in this way can be used up to short lengths, and be easily sharpened.

A good lap for sharpening small cutters nicely is made

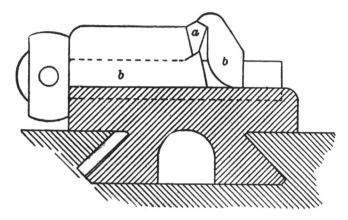

FIG. 93.

of cast iron like a face plate to a lathe, which has filed lines or scratches on the face. It is used with oil and oil-stone powder, or fine emery. It has a shield and runs pretty fast.

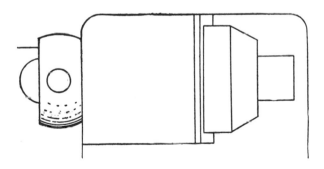

FIG. 94.

Fig. 95, is a back-rest for a bench-lathe c, being an elevation and d, the plan, which are one-half actual size. a, a', are cuts of a special style of jaws having offset points to take work that would strike the nuts, with the straight jaws in use.

It may seem superfluous to describe the manner of using

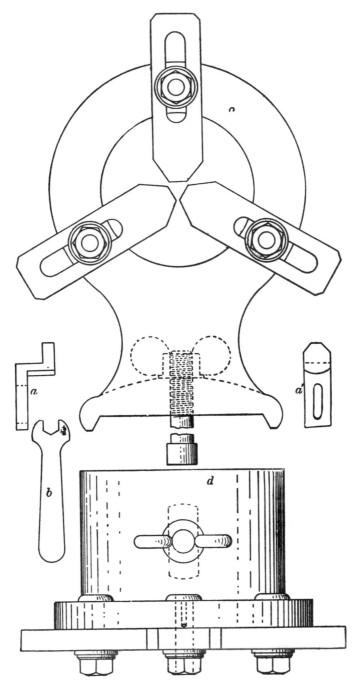

FIG. 95.   *a*, *a′*, *b*, = ¼ scale.

a back-rest, but the writer was in a shop at one time where the only plan for doing so, on an engine-lathe, was one in which the work to be done had a shoulder on the turning to rest against the jaws of back-rest, to keep the former against the lathe-center.

Suppose it is desired to make a boring in the end of a piece of round steel perfectly true with the outside, there being no stock to spare on the latter.

Then center one end lightly with a prick-punch mark, and place this against the running center of the lathe. Bring the other end as near central as convenient with the tail-stock, and let the jaws of the back-rest touch the out side of the piece lightly and fasten in this position. Then while the work is running make a true center with a grav-

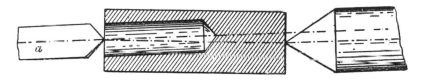

FIG. 96.

er, and if required drill and countersink. While this is being done the work may be out of line with the centers; but to get it in line, bring the lathe center against the center just made in the piece of work, and reset the back-rest jaws in this position when the other end has been centered in the same way. The work is now ready to be bored out perfectly true and parallel with the out side.

But to hold the piece against the running center while these operations are going on it is only necessary to fasten a clamp-dog or driver on the work, loosen the lathe face-plate two or three threads, then, having two holes in the face-plate opposite each other and quarter way around from the driver-opening, pass a piece of lace-leather through these and around the dog, drawing it up against the face-plate and tying the lace-leather to hold it. Then tighten the same by screwing the face-plate back to place.

Where lathe centers are not in line, work drilled on the centers will not come in line, and rimmers will be thrown over, making a hole larger than the rimmer, at the entrance, when the work is on a face plate.

Fig. 96, illustrates this. The drill a, is in line with the running spindle and the opposite center is off and the result is plain.

Fig. 97 is a tool deserving especial attention, and one that should find a place in every shop where a lathe is used. a, and b, give general idea of the tool, which is for testing or truing up work in a lathe. The cut gives a tester the right size for a bench-lathe, in which the tools are made of $\frac{1}{2}$ inch by $\frac{1}{4}$ inch steel. a, and b, is made of this size steel, and is the part that goes in the tool-post. h, h', is a flat spring pinned or soldered, one end into the steel piece and one in the outside ring. There are two rings one within the other, and the straight piece for testing the work in the center. The three pieces are held by the screw-points making a universal movement. c, d, e, and f, are different styles of pieces that fit the taper hole i, in the front end of the straight piece. The opposite end k, has a hole for receiving a long tapering hard wood stick in a small tool, or a steel rod perhaps in a larger one for the engine lathe. There is no particular accuracy required in this tool so long as the joint permits the rod to have a free movement in every direction. The wooden piece should not be too long and tremulous, as the vibration makes it uncertain in its motion. Suppose a piece of work on a lathe face-plate has a pin projecting, and it is desired to have the work revolve true with the center of this pin. Then let the fork c, straddle the pin as it runs; and if the latter is out of true with the lathe center then it will move the fork, and the distance it moves will be multiplied at the outer end of the long wooden arm. From nine to ten inches or twelve inches at the outside is long enough for the testing stick.

As the work is moved into a central position the motion on the end of the arm will disappear until it comes to a

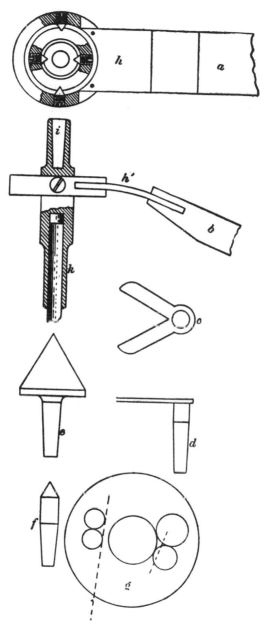

FIG. 97.

stand-still; when it is safe to conclude the work is as near central with the pin and lathe center as possible to have it. *e*, and *f*, are centers for testing up holes in the same way,—*e*, being for holes, and *f*, more especially for small center marks, or prick-punch spots.

As an illustration of the way in which the above tool may be used to secure positively true work take the figure *g*, in the illustration.   It may be required to find the position of the train-holes in a model watch.   Let the largest of the small circles be the center wheel pitch-circle; the next size circle the third wheel, and the next the fourth.   Turn a disc perfectly true the right diameter and center it while running for each wheel. The center-wheel disc can have a hole in the center to put on a pin in the center of the model-plate.   Then shellac or solder the third-wheel disc against it as shown.   The fourth-wheel disc would be right by diameter to set against one of the other discs, but to get its relative position to the other or third disc, grind or file off one side as shown by the dotted lines and bring the flat place against the remaining disc. The exact amount to remove can be calculated and measured with a micrometer gauge.

The model-plate with its discs can now be located on the lathe face-plate and trued by the centers of the discs, one at a time, using the testing tool.

Holes can then be made through discs and all, or the discs removed and the holes made directly in the plate. The two small circles at the left against the longer dotted line show how two or more holes, the required distance from each other, and also from a shoulder or straight-edge, can be obtained in the same way.

These discs can be made with the outside turning and hole in the center concentric, and used as guides for drilling holes, jigs, dies, etc., being located and fastened as before described.

Fig. 98. This is a little tool to be used in a lathe or upright drill-press.   It is simply a rotary file and must run pretty fast.   They are cut on steel-wire or drill-rod, by hand, and are among the most convenient and effective little implements that can be thought of.   They will re-

move stock very fast, and when made about one degree
back-taper are very useful for backing out dies.

A hardened templet or form can be secured on a piece

FIG. 98.

of steel or iron and one of these little files run along its
edge as a kind of profiling tool.

A guide of this kind can be secured to the top of a die

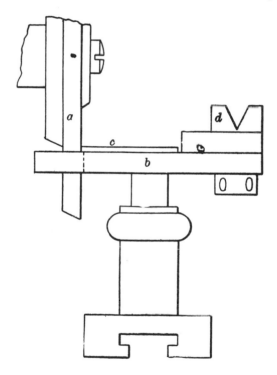

FIG. 99.

and the finishing touches put to it very quickly and safely
this way. The guide can be made of thin sheet steel and
hardened between cast iron blocks as shown in another
chapter;—pin-holes being left for locating it on the work.

Small vertical machines are used quite successfully for filing out small dies. They carry a file up and down rapidly, and the table holding the work can be tipped for backing the dies out. The files can be made of any shape, and ready-made ones used, as well, by having the right shaped holder for them. The files are fastened at both ends one above and one under the table, like a fret-saw, and are readily removed.

Fig. 99, is a tab'e-rest that should accompany the lathe. Let *a*, represent an emery-wheel running in the lathe, and *b*, is the table that slides up and down in the T-rest post. Then *c*, may be a piece of work with lines marked on it that it is desired to file to closely, and squarely. This can be done much better and quicker, when the lines can be ground to, by resting it on the table and against the face of the fine emery-wheel. The table can have a right-angled notch cut in its edge, to accommodate the emery-wheel, and a saw-cut can be made in another place for convenience in using a circular saw.

Model work, especially for watch makers, can be sawed and ground out in this way readily. The same plan on a larger scale can be applied to a regular speed-lathe in the machine shop. *d*, is a movable V that can be used for slotting screws etc. Where screws are made occasionally by hand it is a good plan to tap out a wire two or three

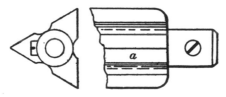

FIG. 100.

inches long for holding them. This can be used for finishing the heads in the lathe, and then in the V guide for pushing them against a saw to slot them. A binding screw that should be shown in the T-rest post is left out in the drawing.

Fig. 100, illustrates a three-sided holder for grinding

taps, that is used in connection with the table rest shown in Fig. 99. The body *a*, may be any convenient length, say three inches, and different sized holes may be used at the two ends. Small taps ground on three sides cut well, and all the taps for small work in a watch-factory are made in this way. The holder rests on the table and the tap is pushed across the edge of the emery-wheel. Simi-

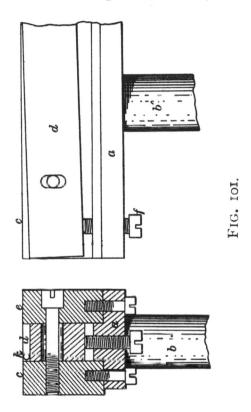

FIG. 101.

lar holders with four and six sides are convenient for numerous purposes.

A small V shaped groove planed in the table itself is a good feature.

Tapering needles or pins of any length and any taper can be made with extreme accuracy in the following way:

Fig. 101. In this illustration *a, a'*, is a piece of soft steel secured to the post *b, b'*, which fits the T-rest holder of

the lathe. c, d, e, are three hardened strips of steel of
any convenient length; two of which c, and d, are shown
in side-view at c', d'.   The strips c, and e, are screwed to
a, and the holes in a, under c, are left oblong, to allow of
moving c, as the face is ground off.   The holes in d, are
left more so to admit of adjusting for the taper, and also
to take up the wear on top.   The screw f, of which there
is one at each end is for adjusting the bar d, for the taper.
The two screws at each end for binding c, e, in place may
be in line with these. c, and e, are made parallel and
hardened, and when screwed in position are lapped perfectly flat and true with each other.   They are also ground
true and flat on the faces that come in contact with d.
The latter is ground perfectly flat on the sides and top.
The wire to be used for making the tapering needle is run
in the lathe and rests in the corner made by the contact
of c, and d.   The screw f, can be used to move d, until
the wire files the right taper.   The pins are held to a gauge
in the chuck when filed, so that the end in the chuck always enters to a positive distance.   In this way all come
alike in relation to the large end of the taper.   The two
hardened strips c, and e, act as a gauge to file to.   The
position of the pin while being filed, is shown in the end-
view at k.   The wear on the surface of c, and d, will come
at this place, or at the two points where the pin runs
against c, and d, and so provision is made to grind the face
of c, and the top of d.

It may be desired to make a hundred needles for jewel-
hole gauges; then after filing this number to the proper
taper they are hardened by placing a sufficient number
in a copper tube to fill the same, sealed up and plunged
when red hot into the water.   By filling the tube with the
needles they come out when hard nice and straight and
clean in appearance, when the temper can be drawn.

They are then put in the chuck again and stoned perfectly smooth and to a uniform taper by using the same
rest, as is shown in Fig. 101.

Needles made in this way are so close in size that they

can be used in the same gauge when held in the same position without regraduating the slide.

The author of this work has in view the getting out of a
similar book on gauges and fine measuring instruments in
which a description of jewel and other gauges will be

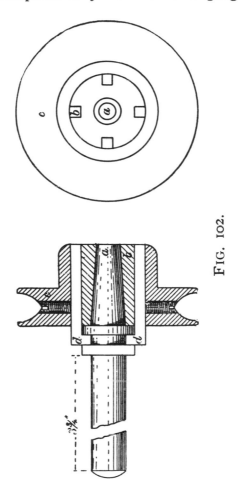

FIG. 102.

found. Especially a variety of measuring and testing tools
used on watch escapements.

Fig. 102, is called a whirl-spindle, and is used on a staff-
lathe for turning watch-balance staffs ctc.   In this case
the work revolves in hollow or female centers which stand
still.   Very small delicate drivers are used for revolving

the work, made of especial shape, and the hollow centers are required on account of the small size of the pivots or points of the staffs.

The spindle is bored out at a, a', to receive a taper center, and where it is intended to use a hardened spindle in this way a straight hole is left in the end before hardening, after which a soft steel plug is soldered into it and the taper hole is bored out in this. Where it is intended to use a pin crossways to drive the tapers out, a hole must be made aiso for this purpose in the spindle to be hardened.

The soft plug can be left projecting from the spindle, and centered, or held in a chuck, for grinding the hardened spindle by. It can be cut off then, and bored out, the spindle being backrested.

The pulley c, c', is bored out to fit the sleeve b, b', which has the four grooves planed in it as shown in the cut.

In two of these opposite grooves the slips d, d, are held by the set-screws in the pulley, and these slips have ends at right angles which run in the groove of the spindle. One slip can be moved against the back of the groove and the other against the front to take up the wear and the endshake, keeping the taper in a position to run freely.

The centers for the staffs to run in are made with two special punches, held in spindles which run in an upright guide or stand, the tapers being held in a block centrally under them. The prick-punches are ground and polished nicely at angles of 40° and 60° respectively, and being made on taper pins can be easily replaced. The 40° punch gives the bearing for the pivot to run in, and the 60° one sinks the bottom of the center deeper. The spindle for holding the punches is 3.75 by .25 inches.

Fig. 103. Sometimes it is necessary to turn off the circumference of work that must be held true against a face plate, and that cannot be carried on an arbor. A balance wheel for example, is located by a hole in the center of the arm. Before the stock is punched out around the arm a hole is made for a pin to enter and turn the wheel in the lathe, and the plate a, in. Fig. 103 rests against the bal-

ance rim and holds it to the face-plate.   A turning is then
made on the brass rim true with the center-hole.   The
cup shaped piece *a*, is held in a rocking position as shown
to secure perfect contact with the work, and the hardened

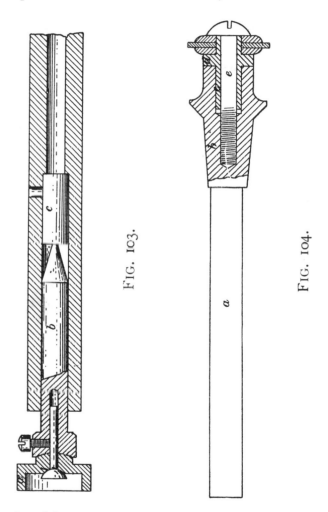

FIG. 103.

FIG. 104.

spindle *b*, with small point runs against the hardened
plug *c*, which makes the friction very trifling.

Fig. 104 gives a method of making a perfectly true saw-
arbor, which is required for some work.   In the illustration the saw is between two cutters whose edges make a
circle, and the three together are used for cutting the

curve and slot in the fork of a watch escapement. It will
be understood that in this instance the cutter should run
pretty truely, and a spindle *a*, is made for this particular
work. Before being hardened it is drilled and tapped out
at *b*, and bored out at *c*; the latter is ground true after the
spindle is hardened. The piece *d*, is made by itself, ground
true on an arbor, and has a hole through it larger than the
screw *e*, which passes freely through the same. This may
seem like taking too much pains for the result; but the
hardened spindle if left thin at the end for the arbor is
liable to crack in hardening when the whole is lost, while

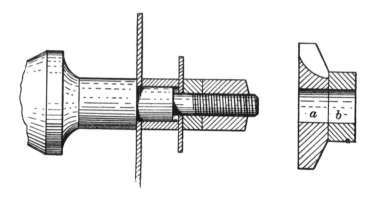

F IG. 105.

in making it as above only the sleeve *d*, can be damaged.
It can also be replaced or changed for another size.

A plain saw–arbor for the bench-lathe can be made on
a chuck-blank, with two turnings on it for two sizes of
saws or cutters, say with .20 and .2⁵ holes for arbor. A collar for the .25 turning can reach by the turning, for saws
with .20 hole to rest against, and another collar with .20
hole can be used on the small end. See Fig. 105. Having
an arbor like this especial tools can be made cheaply and
used in connection with it for a variety of purposes. Take
for example *a*, *b*, in Fig. 105, and let *a*, be a chamfering
cutter or countersink, and *b*, a guide for the same; then
they can be used together on the arbor in the place of
making an expensive tool out of a large piece of steel,

which may be used but a few times. Any style of cutter can be made in this way, with limitations. The angle of *a*, can be varied, the size of *b*, as well, or cutters for sinking a groove or cutting out washers can be used.

Or a longer arbor especially for this kind of work can be made, with pin or key for heavy cuts, to keep the tools from slipping on the arbor.

Another advantage that such a tool gives is the chance to pass the arbor through one hole, attach the cutter and face on the inner end of an opposite piece of work, or to reverse the cutter and dress off the inner end of same piece, to countersink for screw heads etc. Many other applications of the same principle will suggest themselves as occasion requires to the inventive mind,—shell reamers, shoulder cutters, and cutters of irregular form for mould-work etc.

VIII.

A VARIETY OF WAYS AND MEANS.

In Fig. 106 *a*, is a side, and *b*, a back view of a smoothing tooling for planing steel. Used with oil it makes a very nice finish. *b*, shows the steel of which the tool is forged turned one quarter round and shown from the back to illustrate the position in cutting. The tool is what a cutting-off tool would be if twisted out of line the width of the stock, with a wrench. There is no especial width or other dimension required, and it smooths the work by scraping it. It may be said here that a good way to finish a soft steel surface, is to use oil with a hand surface scraper, for bench work.

Another convenient tool for the planer is shown in Fig. 107, which represents a little rest to screw up against the work where it needs support. A set of six or more of these is worth having.

In Fig. 108, is a pair of box-wood jaws for the vise and

for many things much preferable to brass or leather. They
hold the work firmly without marring it, and are very dur-

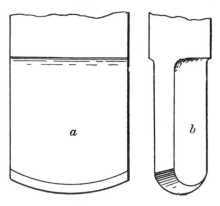

FIG. 106.

able if made of good stock.   They are connected at the
bottom   with a   common brass butt,   and the coiled
spring *a*, separates them as the vise opens.

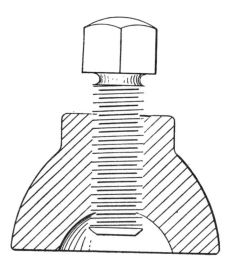

Fig. 107.

Apprentices sometimes find time during noon-hours or
while a lathe is running to make something for themselves,
and Fig. 109 may furnish an acceptable plan for making a

hardened try-square.   The stock a, and the blade b, are separate pieces, to be finished soft, hardened and then lap-

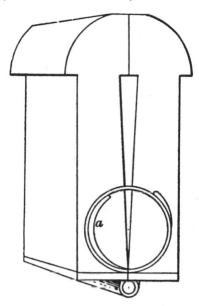

FIG. 108.

ped on a block perfectly parallel. Then they can be adjusted with the long screws and held firmly with the short one,

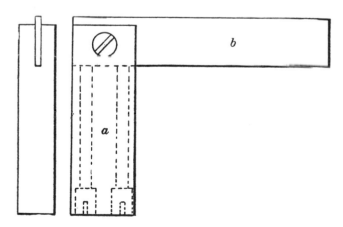

FIG. 109.

which acts also as a close fitting pin for the blade to swivel on.

The writer had occasion at one time to bore out a lot of
brass plates or discs to size for reaming, and found the tool
shown in Fig. 110 very serviceable.

It was used in a kind of revolving tool-holder, that
turned on an eccentric stud on the tail-stock spindle to a
speed-lathe.   It held a drill, boring-tool, reamer etc., in
a limited space.   The holder *a*, Fig. 110 was straight and
entered one of the holes in the revolving tool-holder, so
that by turning in the socket, the point of the cutter *b, b'*,
could be turned up and made right to cut steel, or dropped

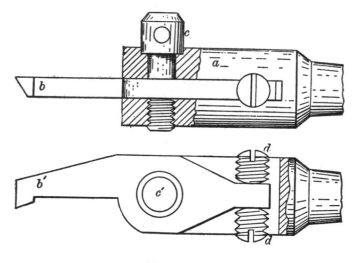

FIG. 110.

down for brass.   The screw *c, c'*, was a stud for *b, b'*, and
a binding screw at once; and the two short screws *d, d*, adjusted it nicely for the cut. The cutter *b, b'*, made of regular size steel wore well and was easily replaced.

Fig. 111, is a cut that belongs properly with the description of the bench-lathe construction.   It is a tool used
for removing the stock in the 3° and 45° bearings.   It is
quite ingenious in its form as it admits of grinding and re-
grinding to sharpen the lips for both angles.   It has six
lips, or blades, which alternate,—three long and three
short ones, like *a*, and *b*.

It will be seen that after the tool is hardened the long

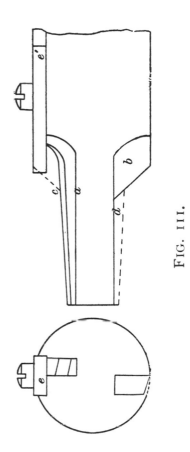

FIG. III.

blade a, can be ground up past the place where it meets the cut made by b, as shown by the dotted line at c, which would be impossible if a, and b, angles were both on one blade. In the same way b, can be ground straight past the point where it meets the cut made by a, as shown by dotted line d. The long and short lips then act as though they were a solid blade with angles in line.

It is plain that such a tool is very valuable where it can be utilized, and where it is required to remove a quantity of stock from a good many pieces. e, e', is a sliding stop for gauging the depth to drive the tool.

Fig. 112 is a novel affair though it has been very useful as well.   It is for winding springs with oval profile or egg-shaped.

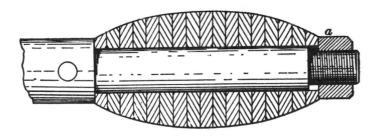

FIG. 112.

It is simply an arbor with a series of washers held in place by the nut a.   They are secured firmly, and turned the proper form collectively, and numbered so as to be replaced conveniently.

Then the spring is coiled closely around them, and removed by taking off the nut, drawing out the arbor, and stretching the coils of the spring apart, when the washers fall out. The form of the washers of course can be modified to suit,—flattened on the side, etc.

Fig. 112A, furnishes a plan for securing perfect allignment and equidistance in holes. Let a, a', be a steel strip planed as shown, the recess being perfectly parallel.

Then make the discs b, having the hole true with the outside, which fits the groove in the strip. Drill a hole, with one of the discs for a guide, in the strip near the cen-

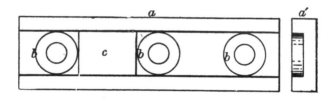

FIG. 112A.

ter. Locate this as desired with a pin; say one turned in center of lathe face-plate. Locate another disc in relation to the first one with block c, and get another hole in the strip as before. Transfer this hole to face-plate of lathe, and secure with guide-pin. Then locate another hole in the strip on the opposite side of center hole, with the block c, as shown, and transfer to face-plate on other material as required and the three holes will be in line, and the two outside ones will be equidistant from the center one.

The plan can be modified at will, and the greatest accuracy can be secured by using the tester shown in another place. (See Fig. 97.) Shellac the discs in place and bore the holes instead of drilling. The strip a, a', must be perfectly true and parallel every way to secure a good result. The gauge c, can be made by turning a disc and taking stock equally from both sides until it enters the

groove in the strip *a,* when the diameter turned will furnish the gauge.

All the measurements in this way are obtained mechani-
cally from the turning diameters, and the planed lines.

Fig. 113. It is sometimes advisable to make a cutter for
the milling machine that will admit of grinding on the
face of the teeth without changing the form of the same.

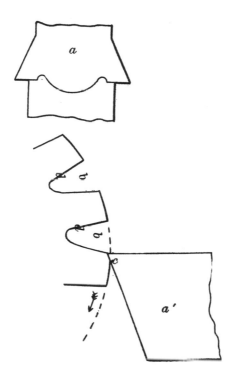

FIG. 113.

Patent cutters of this kind are made with special tools by
the Brown & Sharpe Co., and such as are in general
demand like gear cutters are kept in stock, and can be
bought cheaper than any one can think of making them.
And in some cases they can furnish them to order as profitably.

But the cut in Fig. 113 will give any one a good idea of
a way to make such a cutter for themselves should they

need to. It can be done both cheaply and effectively as follows: Let a, be the top view of a tool for the engine-lathe, having the profile required for the milling cutter to be made, and a', a side view of the same. Then have the blank for the milling-cutter turned into shape with the above tool and the teeth-spaces milled out as shown at b. The tool a, a', is then set the right height in relation to the teeth of the cutter to be backed off, which can be done with a little experimenting.

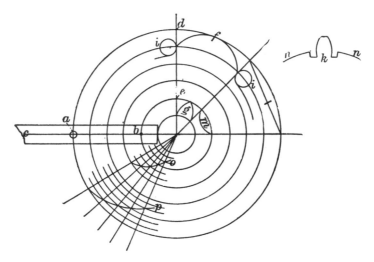

FIG. 114.

The lathe is put in gear if necessary next, and each tooth backed off by hand separately; the milling-cutter being turned in the direction of the arrow. In this way the tool a, a', cuts the heel of each tooth away until the face of the same is reached, and is kept at a uniform depth by gauging itself. For when set right the tool will cut but a little depth when the face will touch the milling cutter as seen at c, gauging all the teeth alike. In this way all the teeth fall back on the same curve, and when used clear themselves, and admit of being ground on the faces d, without changing their form.

Fig. 114, illustrates some of the advantages and some of the disadvantages of working around a center.

Let the bar *c*, swing from the center of the circle and the point *a*, in passing to *d*, will cover the same proportion of a circle that the point *b*, will in passing to *e*.

Neither point will, however, change its distance from the center although the actual distance traveled is several times greater in *a*, *d*, than in *b*, *e*. So the points *a*, *b*, on the bar *c*, will vary their distance from the center as the bar moves in or out, no matter what difference they travel on the circle.

Advantage can be taken of this in making formes for profiling work where a large outline is used directly to secure a small one. That is a guide like *f*, will produce a form like *g*, if their relative positions as shown are maintained. Suppose the bar *c*, to be moved in the distance of a space between the circles, and the small circle *i*, to be a roller with *a*, for its center. Then as *i*, attached to the bar *c*, rolled over the form *f*, the point *b*, would describe the outline *g*. Rolled on the straight line *l*, in the same way the curve at *m*, would result.

Damas-keening machines operating on this principle were used in the Springfield Ill. Watch factory with good results. The fancy work on the nickel finished watches being done in this way. Superior machines in which the same results are secured with a system of gear wheels are now in use.

At *k*, is seen a portion of single tooth wheel used on the adding device of a cash-register. The tooth on this wheel moved another wheel a limited distance at each revolution, entering and passing out at regular divisions on the other wheel; and the wheel carrying it holding the same with its surface *n*, during the passage of *k*. The surface *n*, on this wheel had to be exact in diameter and concentric; and it was the practice to turn this part of the wheel by hand, feeding the tool out and in as it came to the tooth *k*. The tool on finishing the cut naturally jumped into *k*, and in making several turns easily destroyed the shape of the tooth *k*.

The writer designed a machine working on the princi-

ple illustrated above for turning these wheels. The wheel
to be turned was about 1½ inches in diameter, and the
bar carrying the tool guided by a ring or groove 7 or 8 inches in diameter and a curved form like *f*, which jumped
the tool over the tooth *k*, without any difficulty. In this
way a long curve and a good sized roller was used to pass
the tool abruptly by the tooth *k*.

By looking at the lines *o*, *p*, another point showing a
possible disadvantage may be seen. For example, the
writer at one time was making a fixture to use in connection with a small lathe for cutting a spiral groove in a small
disc used on a patent regulator for a watch. A very small
point on the regulator travelled in this groove which had
to be very smooth and regular.

A large form with spiral outline was made by hand by
connecting curves as shown at *p*, which was to all appear-
ances a continuous curve; but when used as a guide it
made the small groove very irregular like *o*, because the
faults in the large curve though invisible were greatly
magnified when reproduced in the small spiral near the
center. To overcome this it was necessary to cut a face-
cam in the engine lathe and transfer this incline indirectly
to the curve on the large spiral, by grinding the same with
an emery wheel.

The point, of interest, however, was that the errors in
the large curve were exaggerated when reproduced near
the center.

The principle illustrated in Fig. 114 being of a general
character may admit of some useful application in the
practice of the reader.

In a treatise on mechanical movements in contempla-
tion the writer expects to illustrate a variety of principles
like the above, as applied in actual practice.

Fig. 115. In a shop where a great deal of tapping in irregular shaped pieces is done, and where it is important to
tap the holes straight, a device like that shown in Fig. 115
will be found very useful. The bed *a*, similar to the table
of a drill-press is provided with slots and holes for fasten-

ing the work as shown, and the arm b, is made to swing over the hole to be tapped, being located by the center. It is fastened in position then with d, and c, acts as a guide for the tap.

Fig. 116, properly belongs in the chapter on hardening and tempering but is too valuable to be omitted. It gives a sketch of a thoroughly practical and inexpensive gas

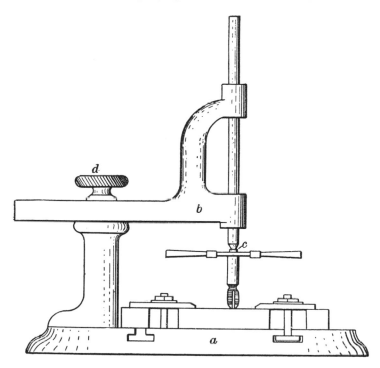

FIG. 115.

generator that will run ten hours a day, six days in the week, for fifteen cents a week. It is 20 inches long by 12 in. wide, and 10 inches high, and is made of galvanized iron. a, gives a general view of the interior from one side. A number of strips the width of the box are hung from the top of the box, 2 inches apart, and reaching within 2 inches of the bottom. They have a short bend at the top by which they are riveted to the box. Half way between these, and reaching from the bottom of the box to within

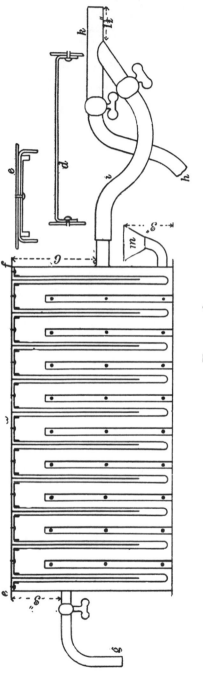

FIG. 116.

2 inches of the top, similar strips run crossways the width
of the box being riveted at each end by the bended edges,

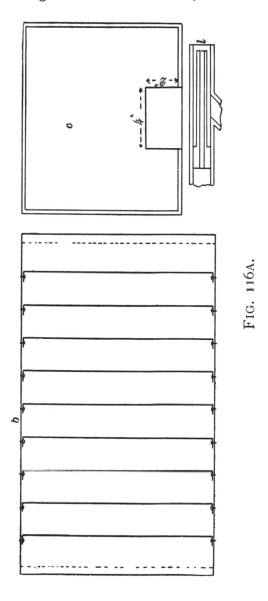

FIG. 116A.

as shown at *d*.   Then commencing at *e*, a strip of cotton
flannel the width of the box is fastened and carried down
to the bottom of the box, where it folds, and then passes

to the top again on the other side of the first partition that drops from the top. It is then riveted between a bow shaped strip and the top of the box, as shown at *e*. This operation is repeated until the cloth is carried to the farthest upper corner of the box opposite the starting point, following the course of inch spaces the length of the box.

The cloth, however, is cut out at each bottom loop as shown on *c*, 4 inches wide, by 2 inches high, which leaves an air passage ½ inch wide by 4 inches long above the gasoline, which is never higher than 1½ inches from the bottom of the box.

Air from a small sized rotary blower is now forced through the box at *g*, the amount being regulated by the valve, a common gas burner one. The pipe from the blower branches off under the machine, one branch connecting with the pipe leading to the box at *g*, and the other with the pipe *h*, for air to mix with the gas.

The air driven in at *g*, forces the gas through *i*, into the tube *k*, which is seen to better advantage at *l*. The tube *k*, is $7/16$ inch inside, and contains a smaller tube with hole about ⅛ inch, and the end of this small tube is $1/16$ of an inch back of the end of large one. The air comes through this small tube, and the gas comes through the one on the side. The rubber pipe *i*, is ½ inch, and *h*, is ¾ inch. *m*, is a tube for filling the tank, and is provided with a stopper. Not over 1½ inch of gasoline is in the box at any time.

This machine has been used with perfect success to the writer's knowledge, and could probably be modified and the smallest blower, such as is used on a hand forge, run by foot-power to operate it.

This fixture is worth many times the price of this book to any one who has use for a good bunsen burner for soldering, tempering, etc., as it is fully equal to the regular city gas for the purpose.

IX.

A VARIETY OF MATTER.

Fig. 117. A few tools for drawing, not found in the stores will be first noticed in this chapter. In Fig. 117, *a*, is a straight wooden rule about 7 in. long with a brass piece like *b*, riveted on to it. The latter has a tongue like *c*, with

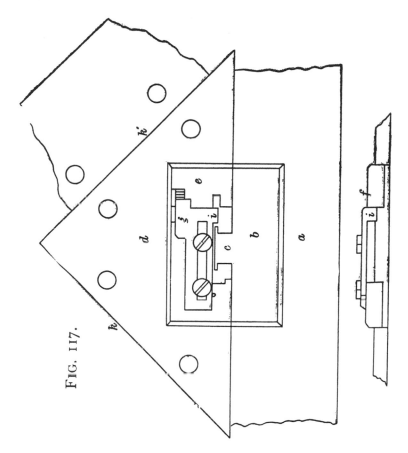

FIG. 117.

projecting points on the sides. *d*, is a triangle drawn about ⅔ size, with a brass piece *e*, and accompaniment, shown in elevation at *f*. This piece of soft sheet brass is turned over on the edges and sunk into the edge of *d*, and riveted to the same. *g*, is a little steel or brass slip, which is adjustable, and can be set by the scale at one end. The point *i*, is made to turn down as shown at i', on f. This piece is made to adjust from nothing to $^2/_{10}$, and regulate the distance for moving d, which is used for drawing section lines by the draughtsman.   The rule a, rests against a straight edge to be shown in Fig. 118 and d, is held against it as shown in Fig. 117.   Both pieces have a hole in them for convenience in sliding them along, not shown in the sketch. Then draw a line along k, or k', slide a, the length of the gauge, and draw d, up to it; and so on for any space required.   If the rule moves out of place it is very easy to start again by the last line drawn. l, is an extra strip for longer lines, fastened to either side of d, by means of a thin metal plate with pins riveted to it that enter the

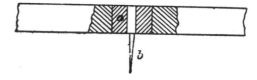

FIG. 118.

holes shown by the circles. Another piece can be attached in the same way, with the same piece, being a kind of complimentary angle which has its drawing edge at right angle with a, so that the gauge can be used for dividing threads of screws etc., or with the edge pitched to angle of screw thread. In connection with the straight-edge shown in Fig. 118 this is a very convenient tool and a cheap substitute for some of the high priced spacing instruments illustrated in the drawing material catalogues. Fig. 118 is a small piece of the straight-edge mentioned shown partly in section. It is simply a rule about 1 ½ inches wide by ¼ inch thick, and any desired length. The writer has two, one about 18 inches, and the other about 30 inches long. Three brass or other metal pieces like a, are driven into the rule, one at each end and one in the center, and held in position with steel needle-pointed pins like b, which being small do not disfigure the paper.

The usefulness of this rule can hardly be appreciated until tried. It is not only of service as used with Fig. 117, but of inestimable advantage for drawing details, and oblique views on large drawings. It can be placed and replaced any where on the board and dispenses with the awkward *T*-square, as large or small angles can be used against it without any danger of its being moved out of place.

Fig. 119. A very handy outfit for small drawings is shown in this figure. *a*, is a maple or other hard wood

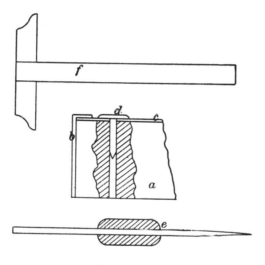

FIG. 119.

block, about 4 by 6 inches and the thickness shown. *b*, is a piece of thin brass such as watch-wheels are punched out of, and three pieces like this are used, one on each side and one on the end. The brass pieces are bent over as shown, and fastened to the block permanently, so that the turned over edge admits a card under it.

Any book-binder or printer will cut up a lot of cards to use in it, for a trifle. Two small steel pins like *d*, with thin flat heads are used to hold the cards, and relocate them at any time. Holes to receive them are made in the block, near the edge where the cards enter. *e*, is a

pointed wire with brass holder on it for pushing out the
pins, pointing new cards through the holes, and opening
the holes for the pins.

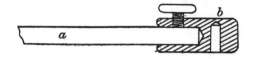

FIG. 120.

f, is a little *T*-square made of cherry, with blade 6½ ×
¾ inches and ⅛ thick, put in a cross-piece 3½ × ¾ × ¼
inch, adapted to the block; and it can be used very con-

FIG. 121.

veniently with ordinary blocks of blank paper, as they usually come square enough for sketching purposes.

Fig. 120. In this figure *a*, is a piece of crescent or stubbs
steel wire planed off a little on one side, and adapted to

use in a pair of Kidd's dividers, which are advertized and illustrated in almost every machinist's supply catalogue. The writer planed up two 3 ft. wires in this way, keeping one of them full length, and cutting the other into shorter lengths for convenience. The adapter *b*, is a piece of steel with screw on top as shown, and one in the side for holding pen and pencil from the set of drawing tools. This makes a good instrument for drawing circles up to 6 ft. in diameter, and one much less costly than the jointed tools at the supply stores. A fine pointed center, with shoulder, can be made for the dividers.

Figs. 121 and 122. These figures illustrate one or two valuable methods employed by engravers in their work and

FIG. 122.

were furnished the writer by a gentleman from Iowa. In Fig. 121 suppose the full lines under *a, c, b*, to be a free hand drawing of half a monogram, made with a soft black pencil; then if it is folded over at the line *a, c*, and rubbed from the back-side on to the paper opposite, a pretty clear impression will appear as shown by the dotted lines. This can be marked in distinctly, and by folding the paper again at *d, b*, the whole can be duplicated, and so on without limit.

In Fig. 122 let the name Mary in full lines represent a name that it is desired to engrave on wood. Then fold the paper as shown above and transfer, when the name will be found reversed. Mark this in with soft pencil and transfer it to the wood to engrave by.

To coat the wood with a thin film that will receive a copy from the pencil marks, use white wax, and mutton-tallow and a drop of fir balsam to make it sticky. This is not a very definite recipe but it was all the writer received, and can probably be utilized with a little experimenting. In this way the second transfer brings the work as first written or drawn.

X.

UNIVERSAL FORMULA FOR GEARING UP ANY LATHE TO CUT ANY THREAD.

Under Figs. 123 124, 125, will be found a description of a universal formula, by the author, for gearing up any lathe to cut any thread. A rule that an apprentice boy, who knows anything about cutting a thread in a lathe, can learn to use in ten minutes, without consulting a table, or the foreman of the shop. It is as follows:

THREAD FORMULA: PART I.

The gear on the screw is to the gear on the stud, as the thread to be cut is to the thread which the lathe will cut with even gears on the screw and stud, simple geared.

PART II.

For lathe with compound gears, changeable, get the ratio for thread by Part I of formula, compound this ratio, and use the proportion that results for the driven and the driving wheels.

PART I.   Suppose a foreman tells a man to cut a screw with eleven threads and gives him a lathe without any gear-plate to select the gears by; all he would need to do, and only once, for that style of lathe, would be to find

two gears with the same number of teeth, and put one on
the screw, and one on the stud, and then mark the thread
on any piece of work in the lathe, which would give him
the key-number to reckon from in cutting any thread.

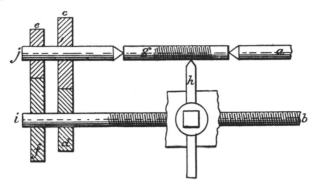

FIG. 123.

For instance: suppose he should use two 24 gears and find
they marked 6 threads to the inch on the piece in the
lathe; then as he wishes to cut 11 threads, the gear for the
screw would be 11 and that for the stud 6, or two gears of
the same proportion—22 to 12; 33 to 18; 44 to 24; etc.

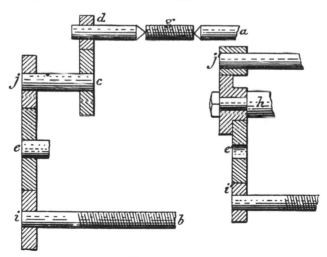

FIG. 124.

By looking at Fig. 125, which represents a gear-plate
from one of Blaisdell's smaller sized engine-lathes, this can

P. BLAISDELL & CO., WORCESTER, MASS.			
S. Gear.	Cut.	Stud.	Screw.
Cuts.	6	24	24
	7	"	28
	8	"	32
	9	"	36
20	10	"	40
22	11	"	44
24	12	"	48
26	13	"	52
28	14	"	56
30	15	"	60
32	16	"	64
34	17	"	68
36	18	"	72

FIG. 125.

be seen illustrated.　The table shows that 24 and 24 gears cut 6 thread; and 44 and 24 cut 11 thread; now 44 is to 24 as 11 is to 6.　To cut an 11⅓ thread, gears 11⅓ to 6 would be required; and to convert the proportion into whole numbers, multiply both 11⅓ and 6 by the denominator of the fraction, which is in this case 3, and get 34 to 18.　Double these numbers and get 68 and 36.　Then 68 on the screw, and 36 on the stud would cut $11\frac{1}{3}$ thread in the above lathe, simple geared. $68 : 36 :: 11\frac{1}{3} : 6$; or

$$\frac{68 \times 6}{36} = \frac{68}{6} = 11\frac{1}{3}.$$

To get a clear view of the principle of gearing a lathe for cutting threads go back to Figs. 123, 124. And first in Fig. 123 imagine something that is not used in practice. Let a, stand for the lathe-spindle, and b, for the screw; and c, and d, for two even gears, or blanks meeting at the pitch-circles of the same. (e, and f, to be absent at present.) Then as the spindle of the lathe turned around it would carry the work g, and the gear c, with it. c, would turn d, and d, would turn b, the screw. The nut in the lathe carriage would travel on the screw b, one thread in one revolution of the screw; and as c, and d, are the same in diameter, a, and b, would revolve alike, and the thread-tool h, would cut a thread on g, the same pitch as that on b, or the screw.

Now suppose c, and d, out of the way, and e, and f, in place. Then, when the spindle a, turned once around, b, would only turn half around, for e, which turns f, has only half the teeth and half the diameter of f. So, if b, was a screw of 6 threads. one revolution of a, would only move the tool h, one-half of a thread on b, which being $\frac{1}{6}$ of an inch, h, would move $\frac{1}{12}$ as g, turned once or 12 threads to the inch on g. With the even gears c, and d, h, would cut 6 threads. It will be seen then, that if even gears, or even revolutions of a, and b, produce threads on a, like those on b, that b, would make 6 revolutions in going an inch, and h, would cut 6 threads on g, at the same time. If it were required to cut 12 threads on g, while b, was going 6, then a, or g, would have to go twice around while b, went once, or, in an inch, a, and g, would go around 12 times while b, would go 6. But as $\frac{1}{6}$ is twice $\frac{1}{12}$, so the gear on b, must be twice as large as the gear on a, as seen at b, and e. The denominator of the fractional part of an inch, that one thread is, gives the name to the pitch; as a

thread $\frac{1}{12}$ would be called 12 pitch, or 12 threads to the
inch. Then as a 6 thread, being $\frac{1}{6}$ of an inch, is to a 12
thread, which is $\frac{1}{12}$,—as 2 to 1, or 12 to 6, so the gears on
b, and a, respectively would be as 2 to 1, or 12 to 6, or that
proportion. And what is true of 12 threads on g, as re-
lated to 6 threads which even gears would cut, under the
circumstances, is true of any other number of threads, and
the same of the gears b, and e. If it had been required to
cut 14 threads, then b, and e, would have been as 14 to 6.
Or if b, had been 8 threads. then even gears would have
cut eight threads, and to cut 14, f, would have 14 and e, 8
teeth. or that proportion.

Now the spindle a, and the screw b, correspond to the
stud and screws on the gear plates; the end i, of b, being
the screw, and the end j of a, being the stud. In Fig. 124
i, and j, are placed more as they appear on the lathe as
screw and stud. j, takes motion indirectly from the spindle and is identified with the thread to be cut. It will be
seen that i, and j, are even gears, but on the other end of
stud j, a gear c, supposed to be twice the size of d, ap-
pears; so that d, and a, revolve twice to one turn of b, the
same as if i, or j, ran directly on to d. And the proportion between i, and j, and the thread to be cut and the one
cut with even gears on i, and j, is the same as though j,
ran directly onto d, or as c, and d, in Fig. 123.

Gears j, and c, are said to be compounded, while j, e,
and i, lying in the same plane. are called a simple train.
The formula then given above, holds good, whether even
gears on j, and i, cut 12 or 6 thread on g, so long as j, and
i, are part of a simple train, or simple geared; so it is not
necessary for the lead-screw and the work to be the same
thread.

But in that part of the cut at the right of Fig. 124 it will
be seen that the gears are compounded before reaching the
regular stud j'', so that i'', and j'', are not simple-geared.

h, is an extra stud carrying two gears, one twice as large
as the other; and it swings on an adjustable bar. The gear
on the regular stud j'', is double width; so that the inter-

mediate wheel e', can swing into it directly as at e, or into the small wheel on h, while the large gear on the same enters j', and doubles its motion. A thread cut with simple gearing then would be doubled with the compound gear. See Fig. 125. 24 and 24 cut 6; with the compound gear between they would cut 12. But on this lathe the simple method cuts up to 18; then the same gears used with the compound stud cut double, saving extra gears.

If a 32 thread for instance was to be cut, and it was found by using the formula that the gears needed were not with the lathe, then divide 32 by 2 and gear up according to the rule for cutting a sixteen thread, and these gears used with the compound stud will give 32.

PART II. 6 on stud, 9 on screw to cut 9 threads simple geared, would be—2 and 3 on stud and pinion, and 3 and 3 on intermediate and screw. Compound geared. Or $6 : 9 :: 2 \times 3 : 3 \times 3$.

Part II of the formula may be used as easily as Part I when once familiarized; and a few examples and explanations will make this possible.

Let us take a lathe in actual use; one with a lead-screw having 2 threads to the inch, and lead-screw and spindle revolving evenly with even gears on stud and screw. Then even gears would cut 2 thread.

The lathe has a set of gears running from 20 to 150, five numbers apart, and threads from 1 to 15 in whole numbers, besides several hundred fractional threads could be cut by Part I of the formula, without using the compound gear.

By using Part II of the formula any thread can be obtained, whole or fractional, that may be required. Threads that can be cut by using Part I, can be cut by using Part II of the formula, substituting pinion and intermediate wheels for stud and screw in Part I, and using even gears on the stud and screw, when using the compound wheel.

In Fig. 124 let the train of gears with compound gear serve to illustrate Part II of the formula. i', is the screw,

e', is simply an intermediate wheel for transmitting motion, and does not come into the calculation directly. On
the stud h, the small wheel is the pinion and the large one
the intermediate proper; while j', is the stud on mandrel
wheel. While not essential, all the changes can be made,
with the lathe under consideration, with one wheel on the
pinion stud, viz., 20.   The stud and the pinion are the
drivers, and the intermediate and the screw are the driven
wheels. The wheels on the stud and pinion can be inter-
changed, and those on the intermediate and screw as well;
but it is more convenient to keep the 20 wheel for the pinion all through.

For an illustration let us find the gears to cut a thread
with 3.75 pitch.

According to Part I of formula the ratio would be $\dfrac{2}{3.75}$
or, 2 on stud and 3.75 on screw.   In common fractions
this would be $\dfrac{2}{3\frac{3}{4}}$.   Reduced to a simple fraction this
would be $2 \times \dfrac{4}{15} = \dfrac{8}{15}$.   The decimal $\dfrac{2}{3.75}$ would be
$\dfrac{200}{375} = \dfrac{8}{15}$. Then with simple gears, there would be 8 on
the stud and 15 on the screw, or their equivalent ratio. This
ratio converted into a proportion would be 2×4 and
3×5, or $2 : 4 :: 3 : 5$.   But there are no such gears in
use, so we enlarge them to $20 : 40 :: 30 : 50$.   And 20 on
the pinion, 40 on the stud, the drivers, with 30 on the intermediate and 50 on the screw, the driven wheels, will
cut a thread with 3.75 pitch. $\dfrac{40}{30} \times \dfrac{20}{50} = \dfrac{8}{15} = \dfrac{2}{3.75}$.

In looking at a table we might find the following com-
bination for a 3.75 pitch: stud 120, intermediate 50,
pinion 20, screw 90.   But the proportion is the same,
$\dfrac{120}{50} \times \dfrac{20}{90} = \dfrac{8}{15} = \dfrac{2}{3.75}$ One of the drivers 40, is increased to 140 by 3: and one of the driven wheels 30, to
90 by 3.

Again to cut a thread 17.538 pitch: $\dfrac{2}{17.538} = \dfrac{2000}{17538}$ ÷

$2 = \dfrac{1000}{8769} = \dfrac{100}{877}$ very nearly. This is $\dfrac{100}{876}$ nearly.

$\dfrac{100}{876} = \dfrac{25}{220} = \dfrac{5}{44} = \dfrac{2 \times 2\frac{1}{2}}{4 \times 11} = \dfrac{20 \times 25}{40 \times 110}$ or gears to
cut 17.538 pitch thread. Changing the fraction so as to divide by 2 affected the pitch only about $\dfrac{1}{10000}$. Notice also that any term with a half in it corresponds with the gears in the 5 division, $2\frac{1}{2} \times 10 = 25$; $6\frac{1}{2} \times 10 = 65$, etc.

In the example of 6 and 9, for instance: $\dfrac{6}{9} = \dfrac{2 \times 3}{3 \times 3} = \dfrac{20 \times 30}{30 \times 30}$; but this makes 3 gears with 30 teeth, more than the set contains. So we can say, $6 \div 9 = \dfrac{2 \times 3}{2 \times 4\frac{1}{2}} = \dfrac{20 \times 30}{20 \times 45}$ or, $\dfrac{20 \times 60}{40 \times 45}$ multiplying the 30 and the 20 by 2, which furnishes the key to selecting the proper wheels.

The writer trusts this will cover all the ground, so far as simplifying the formula goes.

This explanation will appear overdone, perhaps, to some, but the writer trusts it will be acceptable to beginners.

To disengage the lead-screw nut on a lathe and run the carriage back by hand, and lock the nut with lathe tool in position again, do as follows: Stop the lathe, throw nut out, and run carriage back any convenient number of inches and lock the nut again. To do this lay a scale in the ways of the lathe and move the carriage by the same. One inch being the basis of all the thread divisions this is bound to locate the thread tool correctly.

Fig. 126, illustrates a formula for getting the diameter at the bottom of a V thread. Let a, represent 1 thread to the inch, or the unit of measurement. From the top of one thread to the next will be $^{1000}/_{1000}$, for the pitch; and the height, will be $^{866}/_{1000}$ of an inch. The next thread is $\frac{1}{2}$

ınch pitch or 2 pitch, being 2 threads to the inch; and since the proportion is the same in any of the threads, the top of b, being ½ of the top of a, then the height of b, will be

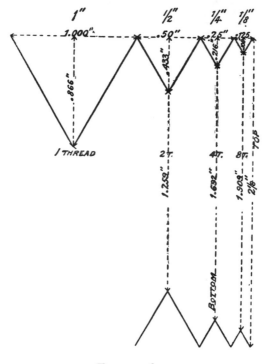

FIG. 126.

½ of the height of a, or ½ of $^{866}/_{1000}$ which is $^{433}/_{1000}$. The same is true of other threads.

But $^{866}/_{1000}$ gives the depth only of one side of the work, and the other must be added, or $^{866}/_{1000}$ doubled which makes 1.732. What is true of a half is true of the whole, so 1.732 divided by the number of threads on the work will give the amount to be deducted from the outside diameter at the bottom of the thread; or, Diameter of the

work,— $\dfrac{1.732}{\text{number of threads}}$ = Bottom of thread.

It will be found generally in practice that this formula will admit of modifying. As in drilling for tapping, or example, a hole somewhat larger than the diameter of the tap at the bottom of the thread is generally made. In cast-iron a fourth of the thread is usually removed, above the smallest diameter size. Dies will generally throw the thread upon steel wire, so that wire smaller than the top of the thread is usually found to work better than full size; although no definite proportion can be furnished to go by.

The tables in the Appendix furnished by Mr. Ballou, will probably be found very acceptable to jewelers and others using small screws.

APPENDIX.

By permission.   Copyright by Geo. F. Ballou and Henry Stark-weather.

TABLE.

OF COMPUTED DIFFERENCES OF TAP AND CORRES-PONDING DRILL-SIZES FOR SHARP V (60°) AND WATCH SCREW THREADS (45°) .

THD.	SHARP V (60°)	WATCH V (45°).	THD.	SHARP V (60°).	WATCH V (45°).
1	1.7320		65	.0266	.0371
1½	1.1547		66	.0262	.0366
2	.8660		67	.0258	.0360
2½	.6928		68	.0254	.0355
3	.5773		69	.0250	.0350
3½	.4948		70	.0247	.0345
4	.4330		71	.0243	.0340
4½	.3849		72	.0240	.0335
5	.3464		73	.0237	.0330
6	.2886		74	.0234	.0325
7	.2474		75	.0231	.0321
8	.2165		76	.0228	.0317
9	.1924		77	.0225	.0313
10	.1732		78	.0222	.0309
11	.1574		79	.0219	.0305
12	.1443		80	.0216	.0302
13	.1332		81	.0214	.0298
14	.1237		82	.0211	.0294
15	.1155		83	.0208	.0291
16	1082		84	.0206	.0287
17	1019		85	.0204	.0283
18	0962		86	.0201	.0280
19	0911		87	.0199	.0277
20	0866		88	.0197	.0274
21	.0825		89	.0194	.0271
22	.0787		90	.0192	.0268
23	0753		91	.0190	.0265

TABLE OF COMPUTED DIFFERENCES, ETC., Continued.

THD.	SHARP V (60°)	WATCH V (45°).	THD.	SHARP V (60°).	WATCH V (45°).
24	.0722		92	.0188	.0262
25	.0693		93	.0186	.0259
26	.0666		94	.0184	.0256
27	.0641		95	.0182	.0253
28	.0618		96	.0180	.0251
29	.0597		97	.0178	.0248
30	.0577		98	.0176	.0246
31	.0559		99	.0174	.0244
32	.0541		100	.0173	.0241
33	.0525		105	.0165	.0230
34	.0509		110	.0157	.0219
35	.0495		115	.0150	.0210
36	.0481		120	.0144	.0201
37	.0468		125	.0138	.0193
38	.0455		130	.0133	.0186
39	.0444		135	.0128	.0179
40	.0433	.0603	140	.0124	.0172
41	.0422	.0588	145	.0119	.0166
42	.0412	.0575	150	.0115	.0161
43	.0402	.0562	155	.0111	.0156
44	.0393	.0549	160	.0108	.0151
45	.0384	.0536	165	.0105	.0146
46	.0376	.0525	170	.0102	.0142
47	.0369	.0514	175	.0099	.0138
48	.0361	.0503	180	.0096	.0134
49	.0353	.0493	185	.0093	.0130
50	.0346	.0483	190	.0091	.0126
51	.0339	.0473	195	.0089	.0123
52	.0333	.0464	200	.0087	.0120
53	.0327	.0455	210	.0083	.0115
54	.0321	.0447	220	.0079	.0110
55	.0315	.0439	230	.0075	.0105
56	.0309	.0431	240	.0072	.0100
57	.0304	.0423	250	.0069	.0096
58	.0298	.0416	260	.0066	.0092
59	.0292	.0409	270	.0064	.0089
60	.0287	.0402	280	.0062	.0086
61	.0283	.0395	290	.0060	.0083
62	.0279	.0389	300	.0058	.0080
63	.0275	.0383	310	.0056	.0077
64	.0270	.0377	320	.0054	.0075

WAYS AND MEANS.

TABLE.

OF WORKING DIFFERENCES OF TAP AND CORRES-PONDING DRILL-SIZES FOR SHARP V (60°) AND WATCH SCREW THREADS (45°).

THD.	SHARP V (60°).	WATCH V (60°).	THD.	SHARP V (60°)	WATCH V (60°).
1	1.707		65	.022	.033
1½	1.131		66	.022	.033
2	.843		67	.022	.032
2½	.670		68	.021	.032
3	.555		69	.021	.031
3½	.474		70	.021	.031
4	.413		71	.020	.030
4½	.365		72	.020	.030
5	.328		73	.020	.029
6	.273		74	.019	.029
7	.229		75	.019	.028
8	.199		76	.019	.028
9	.175		77	.018	.028
10	.157		78	.018	.027
11	.142		79	.018	.027
12	.130		80	.018	.027
13	.120		81	.017	.026
14	.110		82	.017	.026
15	.104		83	.017	.026
16	.098		84	.017	.026
17	.092		85	.017	.025
18	.087		86	.016	.025
19	.082		87	.016	.025
20	.078		88	.016	.025
21	.074		89	.016	.024
22	.070		90	.016	.024
23	.067		91	.016	.024
24	.064		92	.015	.024
25	.062		93	.015	.023
26	.059		94	.015	.023
27	.057		95	.015	.023
28	.055		96	.014	.022
29	.053		97	.014	.022

Table of Working Differences, Etc., Continued.

Thd.	Sharp V (60°).	Watch V (60°)	Thd.	Sharp V (60°).	Watch V (60°).
30	.051		98	.014	.022
31	.049		99	.014	.021
32	.047		100	.014	.021
33	.045		105	.014	.020
34	.044		110	.013	.019
35	.043		115	.012	.018
36	.041		120	.012	.017
37	.040		125	.011	.017
38	.039		130	.011	.016
39	.038		135	.010	.016
40	.037	.054	140	.010	.015
41	.036	.052	145	.010	.014
42	.035	.051	150	.009	.014
43	.034	.050	155	.009	.013
44	.033	.049	160	.009	.013
45	.033	.048	165	.008	.013
46	.032	.047	170	.008	.012
47	.032	.046	175	.008	.012
48	.031	.045	180	.008	.011
49	.030	.044	185	.007	.011
50	.030	.043	190	.007	.011
51	.029	.042	195	.007	.010
52	.029	.041	200	.007	.010
53	.028	.040	210	.006	.010
54	.028	.040	220	.006	.009
55	.027	.039	230	.006	.009
56	.027	.039	240	.005	.008
57	.026	.038	250	.005	.008
58	.026	.037	260	.005	.008
59	.025	.036	270	.005	.008
60	.025	.036	280	.004	.007
61	.024	.035	290	.004	.007
62	.024	.035	300	.004	.007
63	.023	.034	310	.004	.007
64	.023	.034	320	.004	.006

WAYS AND MEANS.

TABLE.

DECIMAL EQUIVALENTS OF 64THS IN INCHES AND CENTIMETERS.

Inches.		Centi-meters.	Inches.		Centi-meters.
64ths	Decimals.		64ths	Decimals.	
I	.015625	.03969	33	.515625	1.30968
2	.03125	.07937	34	.53125	1.34937
3	.046875	.11906	35	.546875	1.38905
4	.0625	.15875	36	.5625	1.42874
5	.078125	.19844	37	.578125	1.46843
6	.09375	.23812	38	.59375	1.50812
7	.109375	.27781	39	.609375	1.54780
8	.125	.31750	40	.625	1.58749
9	.140625	.35718	41	.640625	1.62718
10	.15625	.39687	42	.65625	1.66686
11	.171875	.43656	43	.671875	1.70655
12	.1875	.47625	44	.6875	1.74624
13	.203125	.51593	45	.703125	1.78593
14	.21875	.55562	46	.71875	1.82561
15	.234375	.59531	47	.734375	1.86530
16	.25	.63499	48	.75	1.90499
17	.265625	.67468	49	.765625	1.94468
18	.28125	.71437	50	.78125	1.98436
19	.296875	.75405	51	.796875	2.02405
20	.3125	.79374	52	.8125	2.06374
21	.328125	.83343	53	.828125	2.10343
22	.34375	.87312	54	.84375	2.14311
23	.359375	.91281	55	.859375	2.18280
24	.375	.95249	56	.875	2.22249
25	.390625	.99218	57	.890625	2.26217
26	.40625	1.03187	58	.90625	2.30186
27	.421875	1.07156	59	.921375	2.34155
28	.4375	1.11124	60	.9375	2.38124
29	.453125	1.15093	61	.953125	2.42092
30	.46875	1.19062	62	.96875	2.46061
31	.484375	1.23031	63	.984375	2.50030
32	.50	1.26999	64	1.	2.53999

The following tables are taken, by permission, from the Catalogue of Chailes H. Besley & Co., Chicago.

TABLE.

WEIGHTS OF SHEET COPPER, PER SQUARE FOOT, AND THICKNESS PER ENGLISH WIRE GAUGE.

English Wire Gauge.	Weight Per Sq. Foot.		14x48	24x48	30x60	36x72	48x72
No.	Lbs.	oz.	Lbs.	Lbs.	Lbs.	Lbs.	Lbs.
1	14	8	......	116	181	261	348
2	13	14	......	111	174	250	334
3	12	12	......	102	159	230	306
4	11	9	......	93	145	209	278
5	10	1	......	81	126	182	242
6	9	6	......	75	118	169	226
7	8	11	......	70	109	157	209
8	7	14	......	63	99	142	190
9	7	3	......	58	90	130	173
10	6	8	......	48	81	117	156
11	5	12	......	46	73	104	139
12	5	1	......	41	64	91	122
13	4	5	......	35	54	78	104
14	3	9	......	29	45	65	86
15	3	4	......	26	41	59	78
16	2	14	......	23	36	52	70
17	2	8	......	20	32	45	60
18	2	2	......	18	27	39	52
19	1	15	......	16	24	35	47
20	1	12	......	14	22	32	43
21	1	9	......	13	20	29	39
22	1	7	6½	12	18	26	35
23	1	4	5⅞	10	16	23	31
24	1	2	5¼	9	15	21	28
25	1	0	4⅝	8	12½	19	25
26		14	4	7	11	15	21
27		12	3½	6	9⅜	13	18
28		10	3	5	7	11	15

TABLE.

SHEET AND BAR BRASS.   WEIGHT IN POUNDS.

Thickness, or Diameter, or Side; Inches.	Sheets per Square Foot.	Square Bars, 1 Foot Long.	Round Bars, 1 Foot Long.
1–16	2.7	.015	.011
1–8	5.41	.055	.045
3–16	8.12	.125	.1
1–4	10.76	.225	.175
5–16	13.48	.350	.275
3–8	16.25	.51	.395
7–16	19.	.69	.54
1–2	21.65	.905	.71
9–16	24.3	1.15	.9
5–8	27.12	1.4	1.1
11–16	29.77	1.72	1.35
3–4	32.46	2.05	1.66
13–16	35.18	2.4	1.85
7–8	37.85	2.75	2.15
15–16	40.55	3.15	2.48
1	43.29	3.65	2.85
1–16	45.95	4.08	3.20
1–8	48.69	4.55	3.57
3–16	51.4	5.08	3.97
1–4	54.18	5.65	4.41
5–16	56.85	6.22	4.86
3–8	59.55	6.81	5.35
7–16	62.25	7.45	5.85
1–2	65.	8.13	6.37
9–16	67.75	8.83	6.92
5–8	70.35	9.55	7.48
11–16	73.	10.27	8.05
3–4	75.86	11.	8.65
13–16	78.55	11.82	9.29
7–8	81.25	12.68	9.95
15–16	84.	13.5	10.58
2	86.75	14.35	11.25

TABLE.

Weight of Brass, Copper and Zinc Tubing, Per Foot. Numbered by Brown & Sharpe's Gauge. Weight in Thousandths of Pounds.

BRASS. No. 17.		BRASS. No. 20.		COPPER. Lightning Rod Tube. No. 23.	
Inch.	Lbs.	Inch.	Lbs.	Inch.	Lbs.
1–4	.107	1–8	.032	1–2	.162
5–16	.157	3–16	.039	9–16	.176
3–8	.185	1–4	.063	5–8	.186
7–16	.234	5–16	.106	11–16	.211
1–2	.266	3–8	.126	3–4	.229
9–16	.318	7–16	.158		
5–8	.333	1–2	.189	ZINC. No. 20.	
3–4	.377	9–16	.208		
7–8	.462	5–8	.220		
1	.542	3–4	.252	1–2	.161
1 ⅛	.675	7–8	.284	5–8	.185
1 ¼	.740	1	.378	3–4	.234
1 ½	.915	1 ¼	.500	7–8	.272
1 ¾	.980	1 ½	.580	1	.311
2	1.00			1 ¼	.380
2 ½	1.506			1 ½	.452
3	2.188				

TAP DRILLS.

Table Showing the Different Sizes of Drills That Should be Used When a Full Thread is to be Tapped in a Hole. The Sizes Given are Practically Correct.

Diameter of Tap.	No. of Threads to Inch.			Drill for V Thread.		
1-16	64			No. 56		
3-32	48			50		
1-8	32	48		42	39	
5-32	32	40		32	30	
3-16	24	32		30	26	
7-32	24			18		
1-4	16	18	20	5-32	5-32	11-64
9-32	16	18	20	3-16	13-64	13-64
5-16	16	18		7-32	15-64	
11-32	16	18		1-4	17-64	
3-8	14	16	18	1-4	9-32	9-32
13-32	14	16	18	19-64	21-64	21-64
7-16	14	16		21-64	11-32	
15-32	14	16		23-64	3-8	
1-2	12	13	14	3-8	25-64	25-64
17-32	12	13	14	13-32	27-64	27-64
9-16	12	14		7-16	29-64	
19-32	12	14		15-32	31-64	
5-8	10	11	12	15-32	1-2	1-2
21-32	10	11	12	1-2	17-32	17-32
11-16	11	12		9-16	9-16	
23-32	11	12		19-32	19-32	
3-4	10	11	12	19-32	5-8	5-8
25-32	10	11	12	5-8	21-32	21-32
13-16	10			21-32		
27-32	10			11-16		
7-8	9	10		45-64	23-32	
29-32	9	10		47-64	3-4	
15-16	9			49-64		
31-32	9			51-64		
1	8			13-16		

TABLE OF TAP DRILLS, Continued.

Diameter of Tap.	No. of Threads to Inch.		Drill for V Thread.	
I 1–32	8		53–64	
I 1–16	8		55–64	
I 3–32	8		57–64	
I 1–8	7	8	29–32	15–16
I 5–32	7	8	15–16	31–32
I 3–16	7	8	31–32	I
I 7–32	7	8	I	I I 32
I 1–4	7		I 1–32	
I 9–32	7		I 1–16	
I 5–16	7		I 3–32	
I 11–32	7		I 1–8	
I 3–8	6		I 1–8	
I 13–32	6		I 5–32	
I 7–16	6		I 5–32	
I 15–32	6		I 3–16	
I 1–2	6		I 15–64	
I 17–32	6		I 9–32	
I 9–16	6		I 9–32	
I 19–32	6		I 5–16	
I 5–8	5	5½	I 9–32	I 5–16
I 21–32	5	5½	I 5–16	I 11–32
I 11–16	5	5½	I 11–32	I 3–8
I 23–32	5	5½	I 3–8	I 13–32
I 3–4	5		I 13–32	
I 25–32	5		I 7–16	
I 13–16	5		I 15–32	
I 27–32	5		I 1–2	
I 7–8	4½	5	I 17–32	I 17–32
I 29–32	4½	5	I 9–16	I 9–16
I 15–16	4½	5	I 19–32	I 19–32
I 31–32	4½	5	I 5–8	I 5–8
2	4½		I 21–32	

SPEED OF DRILLS.

THE FOLLOWING TABLE SHOWS THE REVOLUTIONS
PER MINUTE FOR DRILLS FROM 1-16 INCH TO 2
INCH DIAMETER, AS USUALLY APPLIED.

Diameter of Drills.	Speed for Steel.	Speed for Iron.	Speed for Brass.
1–16 in.	940	1280	1560
1–8 "	460	660	785
3–16 "	310	420	540
1–4 "	230	320	400
5–16 "	190	260	320
3–8 "	150	220	260
7–16 "	130	185	230
1–2 "	115	160	200
9–16 "	100	140	180
5–8 "	95	130	160
11–16 "	85	115	145
3–4 "	75	105	130
13–16 "	70	100	120
7–8 "	65	90	115
15–16 "	62	85	110
1 "	58	80	100
1 1–16 "	54	75	95
1 1–8 "	52	70	90
1 3–16 "	49	66	85
1 1–4 "	46	62	80
1 5–16 "	44	60	75
1 3–8 "	42	58	72
1 7–16 "	40	56	69
1 1–2 "	39	54	66
1 9–16 "	37	51	63
1 5–8 "	36	49	60
1 11–16 "	34	47	58
1 3–4 "	33	45	56
1 13–16 "	32	43	54
1 7–8 "	31	41	52
1 15–16 "	30	40	51
2	29	39	49

One inch to be drilled in soft cast iron will usually require·
For ¼ inch Drill, 125 revolutions; for ½ inch Drill, 120 revolutions;
for ¾ inch Drill, 100 revolutions; for 1 inch Drill, 95 revolutions.